D1289668

THE PLATINUM METALS AND THEIR ALLOYS

By
R. F. VINES
Research Laboratory

Edited by
E. M. WISE
Staff Advisor

THE INTERNATIONAL NICKEL COMPANY, INC.
67 Wall Street - - New York 5, N. Y.

Printed in the United States of America

CONTENTS

CONTENTS *(continued)*

FOREWORD

As the platinum group metals and their alloys enter more broadly into industry, knowledge of their physical properties becomes increasingly important. To meet this need for consolidated data concerning platinum, palladium, iridium, rhodium, osmium and ruthenium, the more important information has been summarized and reduced to a convenient form.

Data on the properties of individual metals and those of certain of their binary alloys are given, based upon information available in the literature and from our own and other laboratories. Where discrepancies exist, an effort has been made to select and weight the data and to report representative values.

As more work is done, utilizing modern metallurgical technique, revision is to be expected, particularly in connection with some of the alloy systems, and it is hoped that at a later time sufficient information may be available to permit the inclusion of the more important ternary systems.

Thanks are given to the numerous researchers whose work has been freely drawn upon and to those who have given us the benefit of their experience in reviewing various portions of the data.

It is hoped that this summary of information may be of assistance to those in industry who encounter problems which cannot be met by the less noble metals, but which one of the platinum metals or its alloys may solve.

E. M. Wise
Staff Advisor, Research Laboratory,
The International Nickel Company, Inc.

THE PLATINUM METALS

THE six platinum metals—platinum, palladium, iridium, rhodium, osmium, ruthenium—generally occur together in nature. Platinum is usually the predominant element, although the ratio varies greatly in different deposits. Authorities disagree somewhat on the relative abundance of the platinum metals in the earth's crust, but it is certain that the amount recovered is greatest for platinum followed closely by palladium and much smaller amounts of iridium, rhodium, osmium and ruthenium.

Crude platinum was first discovered in alluvial deposits in South America, and the sands of the Choco river in Colombia still supply appreciable quantities of platinum. These alluvial deposits were the only source of the platinum metals until 1823, when the rich deposits in the Ural mountains were discovered. Russia, which soon became the dominant producer, maintained its position until about 1930 when the copper-nickel ores of the Sudbury district of Canada became an important source. Currently, Canada is the world's largest producer of the platinum metals. For a time rather large quantities of platinum were mined in South Africa, but the richer deposits were soon exhausted and production fell sharply. However, this region still contains large reserves of lower grade ore. The United States produces little platinum aside from that coming from Alaska, where platinum with a substantial percentage of iridium is found in certain river beds.

The six platinum metals arrange themselves in the periodic system in two triad groups; one comprising ruthenium, rhodium and palladium and the other comprising osmium, iridium and platinum. Their positions in the periodic classification of elements and their neighbors are shown in the table on page 10. The platinum metals together with the adjacent lower melting pair of elements, gold and silver, are called the precious metals or sometimes the noble metals.

Platinum Metals and Their Neighbors in the Periodic Table

	Group VIa	Group VIIa	Group VIII			Group 1b
Atomic Number...	24	25	26	27	28	29
Element..........	Cr	Mn	Fe	Co	Ni	Cu
Atomic Weight....	52.01	54.93	55.84	58.94	58.69	63.57
Atomic Number...	42	43	**44**	**45**	**46**	47
Element..........	Mo	Ma	**Ru**	**Rh**	**Pd**	Ag
Atomic Weight....	95.95	...	**101.7**	**102.91**	**106.7**	107.88
Atomic Number...	74	75	**76**	**77**	**78**	79
Element	W	Re	**Os**	**Ir**	**Pt**	Au
Atomic Weight....	183.92	186.31	**190.2**	**193.1**	**195.23**	197.2

In the triad comprising ruthenium, rhodium and palladium the atomic weights are in the neighborhood of 100 and the densities are about 12 gms/cm^3 while in the triad osmium, iridium and platinum the atomic weights are about 190 and the densities about 22 gms/cm^3. Accordingly, the former triad is frequently referred to as the light group while the latter triad is referred to as the heavy group. In each triad the melting point decreases with increase in atomic weight, but it is high in all cases ranging from 1554°C for palladium to about 2700°C for osmium. The specific heat of the elements in the first triad is about twice that of the elements in the second triad.

Platinum and palladium are very ductile and easily worked; rhodium and iridium can only be cold worked after preliminary hot working; while ruthenium is difficult to work and osmium appears to be unworkable. In general, platinum and palladium are more likely to form extensive ductile solid solutions with other metals than the other members of the group, and palladium is outstanding in this respect. Electrical resistivity appears to be dependent upon the position in the triads, for platinum and palladium have a resistivity about twice that of iridium and rhodium. Similarly, the lattice structures of osmium and ruthenium are of the close packed hexagonal type, while the other metals have a face centered cubic lattice. Osmium and, to a lesser extent, ruthenium form readily volatile oxides, which is not the case with the other metals. Thus it appears that, in many respects, the similarity between the corresponding members of the light and heavy triads is more striking than that between the members of the same triad.

All six metals are very resistant to corrosion by common acids and chemicals. Platinum is not attacked by any single acid but is dissolved by aqua regia, although at a lower rate than gold. Palladium is resistant to the common acids with the exception of nitric acid and hot concentrated sulphuric acid. Iridium, rhodium and ruthenium are most resistant and are not attacked by aqua regia. Another chemical characteristic of the platinum metals is their ability to form stable complex salts which are important in electroplating and refining.

More detailed information on the physical and mechanical properties of the platinum metals and their alloys is given in the following sections. Except for general statements concerning the corrosion and tarnish resistance, chemical properties are not discussed. The many and diverse established uses of the platinum metals and their alloys are given and some proposed uses are also included. It is hoped that these data will suggest additional industrial applications where the platinum metals may be used to reduce costs or achieve results not possible with less noble metals.

In addition to the numerous references cited, a selected bibliography of general works on platinum metals and their uses is included which will be useful to those who are concerned with the application of these metals.

USES OF THE PLATINUM METALS

USE	Pt	Pt Ir	Pt Rh	Pt Ru	Pt Au	Pt Ag	Pd	Pd Ru	Pd Au	Pd Ag	Other Platinum Metals, Alloys or Materials
ELECTRICAL AND PHYSICAL											
Contacts for communication and other relays, magnetos, thermostats, voltage regulators, and control devices	x	x	x	x		x	x			x	WC+Pt or Os, PtAuAg, PdCu, OsIrRu, etc.
Spark Plug Electrodes	x	x	x								
Resistors	x	x					x			x	
Furnace heating resistors	x		x								Rhodium
Resistance thermometers	x										
Thermocouples	x		x						x		
Temperature limiting fuses									x		PtPdAu
Overload electrical fuses	x	x									
Detonator fuses		x									
Thermionic cathodes											PtNi
Metal to glass seals	x										"Liquid" Platinum
Reflectors											Rhodium
Light filters											Rhodium or Platinum films
CHEMICAL											
Corrosion resistant equipment, solid or clad	x	x	x						x		
Crucibles	x	x	x								
Safety (bursting or frangible) discs	x	x									
Anodes for "per salts," halogens, organic oxidations, electroplating and electroanalysis	x	x	x								
Cathodes for electroanalysis	x	x									
Spinnerets for rayon			x		x				x		PtPdAu
Surfaced glass joints to prevent sticking											"Liquid" Platinum
Feeder dies for glass lamp bases and spinnerets for glass fiber	x		x								PtIrNi
Crucibles for oxide fusions, including glass, and synthetic crystals for optical parts	x	x	x								Iridium
Burner nozzles	x	x									
Gas meters and orifices	x	x	x								
CATALYSTS											
Oxidation of ammonia for nitric acid production			x								

USES OF THE PLATINUM METALS

USE	Pt	Pt Ir	Pt Rh	Pt Ru	Pt Au	Pt Ag	Pd	Pd Ru	Pd Au	Pd Ag	Other Platinum Metals, Alloys or Materials
Oxidation of sulphur dioxide for sulphuric acid production	x										
Automatic gas lighters and flameless cigarette lighters	x										
Hydrogenation of numerous organic compounds	x						x				Ruthenium
Dehydrogenation of numerous organic compounds	x						x				
DENTAL											
Casting alloys		x									PtPdAuAgCu
Wrought alloys	x	x					x		x	x	PtPdAuAgCu, PdRhRu and PdPtAg
Tooth pins and anchorages		x					x		x	x	PdPtAuAg, PdPtAu and PdAuAg
Porcelain matrices	x										
Reinforcement for dental porcelain	x	x									
JEWELRY AND DECORATIVE											
Diamond and other gem mountings		x		x				x			PdRuRh
Ring blanks	x	x						x			PdRuRh
Decoration in conjunction with gold	x	x		x				x		x	PdRuRh and PdPtAg
Spectacle frames	x	x		x				x		x	PdPtAg
Watch Cases		x		x				x		x	PdRuRh and PdPtAg
Non-tarnishing leaf for signs, bookbinding, leather goods, etc.	x						x				
Metallized glass and ceramic ware											"Liquid" Platinum
Medals, trophies, objects of art, etc.	x	x		x			x	x			PdRuRh
Electroplates	x						x				Rhodium
Platinum solders									x		PtPdAuAg also Au
MISCELLANEOUS											
Hydrogen purification by diffusion							x				
Photographic papers	x						x				
Color responsive CO detectors											Palladium Chloride
Finger print detection and biological stain											Ru or Os compounds
Grain refiners for gold and silver base dental alloys											Iridium and Ruthenium
Tips for fountain pens and phonograph needles											RuOs with Ir, Pt, W, Co or Ni

PLATINUM

Platinum is the most important and most abundant metal of the platinum group. With an atomic number of 78, it is the end member of the third series of transition elements in the periodic table and has an atomic weight of 195.23 (1).

Grades of Platinum. Platinum refiners and workers recognize at least four different grades of platinum but unfortunately the designations used have not been standardized. The minimum platinum content and the refiners designations for the various grades are shown in Table 1. Since refiners frequently supply metal with a platinum content higher than the minimum specified in Table 1, it should perhaps be emphasized that, except for Grade 1 platinum where the permissible amount of impurity is minute, this system does not postulate well defined grades.

TABLE 1
Grades of Platinum

Grade	Minimum Platinum Content Percent	Refiners Designations
1	99.99	Thermo-Element, Physically Pure or Chemically Pure
2	99.9	Chemically Pure, Special Pure or Specially Refined
3	99.5	Crucible
4	99	Commercial or Commercially Pure

Grade 1 platinum is the purest grade of platinum commercially available and commands a price premium over the other grades. It is used for thermocouple or resistance thermometer wire where extremely high purity is essential. For all other uses where a pure platinum is desired, Grade 2, which is refined to within one step of Grade 1, is generally employed. The main impurities in this grade are traces of other platinum metals predominantly iridium and rhodium. Grade 3 platinum is an especially alloyed platinum used for crucibles and laboratory ware. In the early days of the industry, the iridium and rhodium usually present in crude platinum were not completely removed from platinum intended for such uses. However, the lack of uniformity in material so produced and improvements in refining technique led manufacturers to abandon this procedure and this grade is now made by adding controlled amounts (0.3 to 0.5 percent) of iridium or rhodium to Grade 2 platinum. The composition of Grade 4 platinum is less rigidly controlled as it is used for applications where commercial purity is adequate and where some latitude in physical properties is permissible. The impurities in this grade are mainly other platinum metals but it may also contain traces of other metals.

Silicon is difficult to completely eliminate from certain types of crude platinum and traces of this element as well as calcium or other impurities picked up from the refractories in melting or otherwise introduced may also be present in some grades of platinum. The amounts and nature of these impurities are more important in determining the mechanical properties of platinum than small amounts of other platinum metals. For this reason, the methods employed in refining, melting and to a lesser extent subsequent processing will have an effect upon the final mechanical properties. In applications where the final mechanical properties must be maintained within narrow limits, as in bursting disks and dental foil, special attention must be given to these details by the producer, who should be fully advised of the proposed application.

DENSITY Values ranging from 21.3 to 21.5 gm/cm^3 at 20°C have been reported for the density of annealed platinum; the best value being about 21.45 gm/cm^3 at 20°C. As in other metals, the density varies somewhat with the mechanical state, and cold worked platinum has a slightly lower density than annealed platinum. According to Kahlbaum and Strum (2) the density of annealed platinum is 21.43 gm/cm^3 at 20°C while that of cold worked platinum is 21.41 gm/cm^3 at 20°C. The density calculated from the lattice constant is 21.447 gm/cm^3 at 20°C and 21.459 gm/cm^3 at 0°C (3).

LATTICE The face centered cubic lattice of platinum has a unit cell a_0 of 3.9158 ± 0.0003 A at 20°C according to Owen and Yates (3).

ALLOTROPY Published data indicate that platinum is devoid of allotropic transformations.

MELTING POINT The melting point of platinum is 1773.5° ± 1°C according to Roeser, Caldwell and Wensel (4). Hoffmann and Tingwaldt (5) found 1773.8°C while Schofield (6) obtained 1773.3°C.

BOILING POINT Jones, Langmuir and Mackay (7) estimated the boiling point of platinum from their excellent determinations of the vapor pressure to be about 4530°C.

VAPOR PRESSURE The vapor pressure of platinum, in millimeters of mercury, is 1.1 x 10^{-12} at 1000°C, 1.1 x 10^{-6} at 1500°C, 1.3 x 10^{-4} at the melting point, 2.1 x 10^{-3} at 2000°C and 760 at 4530°C according to Jones, Langmuir and Mackay (7). The rate of evaporation of platinum in vacuo in grams per cm^2 per second as determined by the above investigators is given in Table 2.

According to Crookes (8), in air at 1300°C, platinum is twice as volatile as rhodium, one-third as volatile as palladium, one-thirtieth as volatile as iridium and one-hundredth as volatile as ruthenium. It should be emphasized, however, that this order of volatility applies to tests in air where the oxidation of some of these metals and volatilization of the oxides is a factor. Thus Stewart (9) found that the loss on heating platinum in air decreased with decreasing pressure, and that the loss

TABLE 2
Volatilization of Platinum in Vacuo

Temp. ° C........	527	727	1227	1727	2727	3727	B. P. 4527
Loss gms/cm^2/sec.	1.39x10^{-26}	6.7x10^{-20}	5.23x10^{-11}	1.24x10^{-6}	1.5x10^{-2}	1.2	8.9

was very small in nitrogen and no loss occurred in hydrogen. Similarly, Holborn and Austin (10) report that the loss on heating platinum is five times as great in oxygen as in air, about one-half as much in air at 25 mm as in air at 760 mm and very small in nitrogen.

THERMAL CONDUCTIVITY Jaeger and Dieselhorst (11) give 0.166 cal/sec cm² °C/cm at 18°C and 0.173 at 100°C for the thermal conductivity of platinum. Barrat and Winter (12) give similar values of 0.165 at 17°C and 0.170 at 100°C.

THERMAL EXPANSION The average value given for the instantaneous coefficient of linear expansion of platinum at 0°C is 8.9×10^{-6} per °C and in the range between 0 and 100°C, the mean value is close to 9.0×10^{-6} per °C. For temperatures up to 1000°C, Holborn and Day (13) give the equation:

$$l_t = l_0 (1 + 8.868 \times 10^{-6} t + 1.324 \times 10^{-9} t^2)$$

where l_t is the length at temperature t in relation to the length at 0°C, l_0. Holborn, Scheel and Henning (14) measured the change in length of a platinum specimen, 1 meter long at 0°C, over the temperature range −190 to 1000°C and obtained values shown in Table 3.

TABLE 3
Thermal Expansion of Platinum

Temperature ° C.	Ratio Lt/Lo
−190	.99849
−175	.99860
−150	.99878
−125	.99897
−100	.99916
− 75	.99936
− 50	.99957
− 25	.99978
0	1.00000
25	1.000221
50	1.000444
75	1.000671
100	1.000899
200	1.00183
300	1.00278
400	1.00376
500	1.00477
600	1.00580
700	1.00686
800	1.00794
900	1.00905
1000	1.01019

Holborn's and Day's data together with expansion curves for palladium, iridium and rhodium are shown in Figure 1. Of these metals, palladium has the highest thermal expansion followed by platinum, rhodium and iridium. Esser, Eilender and Bungardt (189) measured the change in lattice parameter with temperature up to 1000°C and found that expansion coefficients calculated from these data were generally somewhat higher than those determined dilatometrically. However, this difference gradually decreased with increasing temperature.

SPECIFIC HEAT According to Jaeger, Rosenbohm and Bottema (15) reproducible results for the specific heat of platinum are not obtained unless the metal is first heated to 1600°C and slowly cooled. This treatment is necessary to bring the metal into a "stable" condition but is not considered to be indicative of allotropic transformations. The true specific heat of platinum so treated can be represented by the relation

$$c_p \text{ in cal/gm} = 0.031678 + 6.30574 \times 10^{-6} t - 1.624878 \times 10^{-10} t^2$$

for temperatures up to 1400°C. Values for the specific heat calculated from this formula are given in Table 4.

More recent determinations, by Jaeger and Rosenbohm (190), for the heat

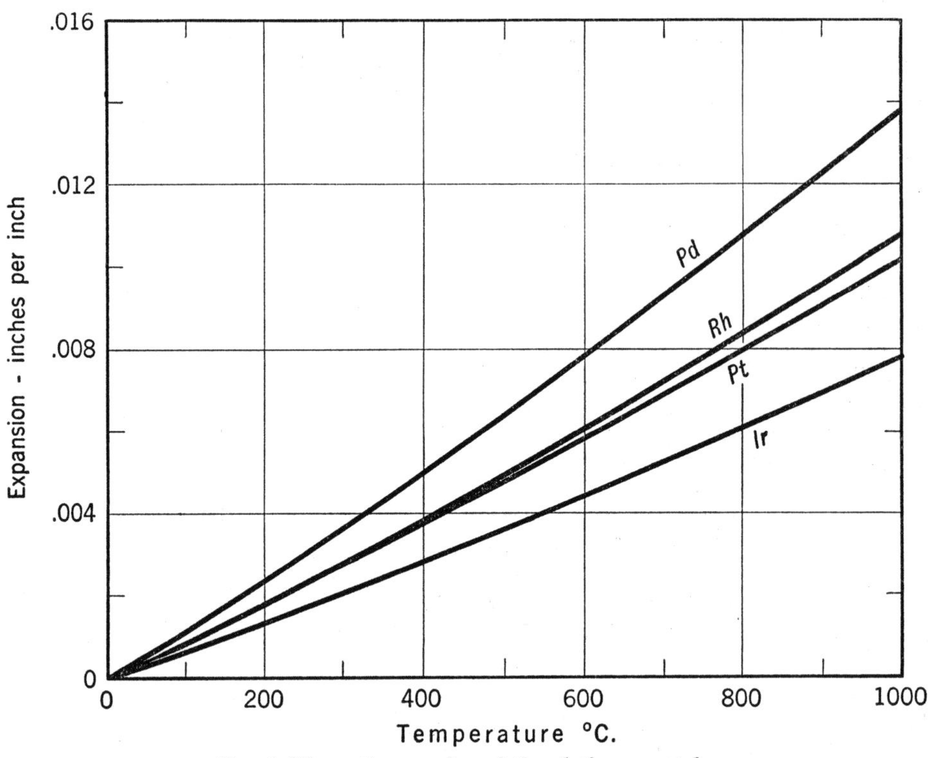

Fig. 1. *Thermal expansion of the platinum metals.*

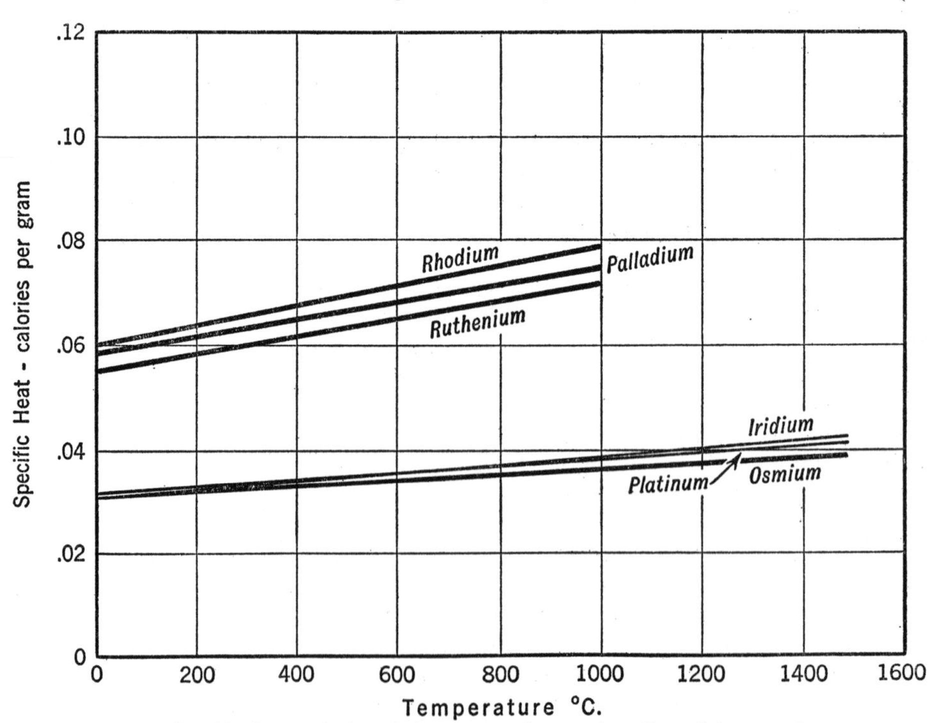

Fig. 2. *Specific heats of the platinum metals as a function of temperature.*

content of platinum, "Q", are considered to be accurate to within 0.1%. These data may be represented by the following formulae:

between 0 and 500°C

$$Q_{t^\circ-0^\circ} = 0.031357t + 0.04507 \times 10^{-4}t^2 - 0.0161 \times 10^{-7}t^3$$

between 400 and 1600°C

$$Q_{t^\circ-0^\circ} = 0.031622t + 0.03172 \times 10^{-4}t^2$$

The change in specific heat with temperature for platinum and the other platinum metals is shown in Figure 2.

TABLE 4
Specific Heat of Platinum

Temperature °C.	Specific Heat cal/gm
0	0.031678
100	0.0323
200	0.0329
300	0.0335
400	0.0342
500	0.0348
600	0.0354
700	0.0360
800	0.0366
900	0.0372
1000	0.0378
1100	0.0384
1200	0.0390
1300	0.0396
1400	0.0402

ELECTRICAL PROPERTIES

ELECTRICAL RESISTIVITY Grade 1 platinum has an electrical resistivity of 9.81 microhm-cm at 0°C in the annealed condition. Electrical resistivities for other temperatures, calculated from this value and the formula $R_t = R_0 (1 + 3.9788 \times 10^{-3}t - 5.88 \times 10^{-7}t^2)$ are given in Table 5.

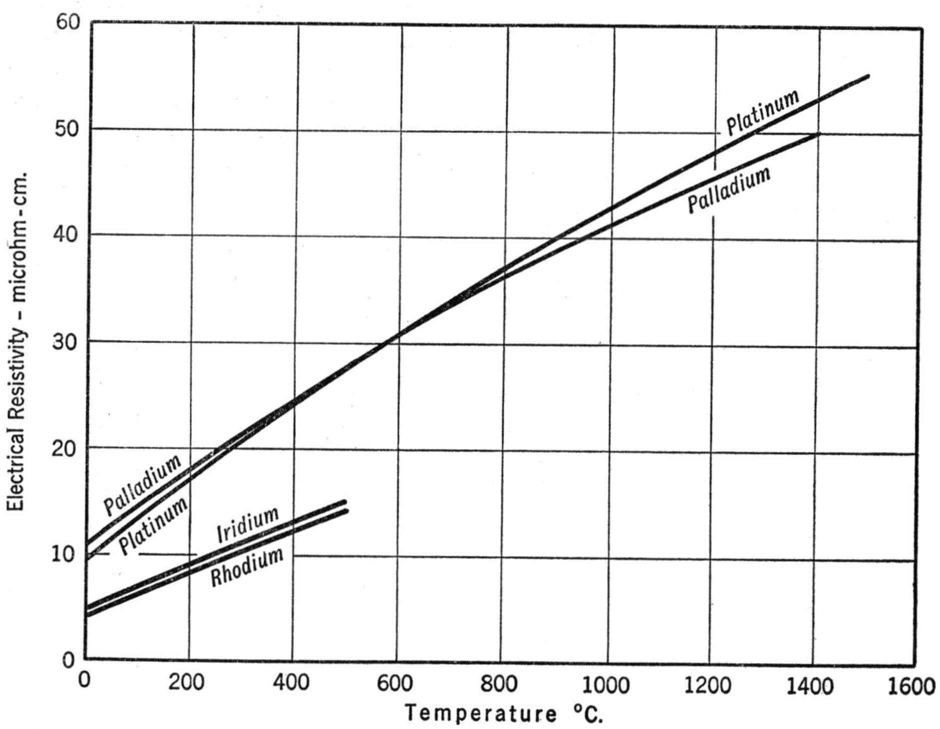

FIG. 3. *Effect of temperature on the electrical resistivity of the platinum metals.*

The resistivity of other grades of platinum is, of course, higher; that of Grade 4 averaging about 15 microhm-cm at 20°C. The resistivity of platinum is slightly less than that of palladium and about twice that of rhodium or iridium. The change in resistivity with temperature for platinum and the other platinum metals is shown graphically in Figure 3.

TABLE 5
Effect of Temperature on the Electrical Resistivity of Platinum

Temperature ° C.	Resistivity Microhm-cm
0	9.81
20	10.59
100	13.65
200	17.38
300	21.00
400	24.50
500	27.88
600	31.15
700	34.30
800	37.34
900	40.27
1000	43.07
1100	45.76
1200	48.34
1300	50.80
1400	53.15
1500	55.38

Meissner (194) studied the effect of drawing and annealing on the resistivity of platinum and found that cold work increased the resistivity slightly but that it rapidly returned to normal on annealing.

EFFECT OF ALLOYING ADDITIONS ON RESISTIVITY

Figure 4 shows the effect of the additions of other metals to platinum on the specific electrical resistivity. Of these metals, copper produces the greatest increase per unit weight and rhodium the least. Of the platinum metals, ruthenium gives the greatest increase per unit weight, followed by osmium, iridium, palladium and rhodium.

TEMPERATURE COEFFICIENT OF ELECTRICAL RESISTANCE

The temperature coefficient of electrical resistance $\left(\frac{R_{100} - R_0}{100\ R_0}\right)$ of Grade 1 annealed platinum is 0.00392 per °C. This ratio is widely used as an indicator of the purity of platinum and for the purest platinum yet produced is about 0.003925 (16). The electrical resistivity of Grade 1 platinum at temperatures up to 1500°C in relation to the resistivity at 0°C is given by the equation:

$$R_t = R_o\ (1 + 3.9788 \times 10^{-3}t - 5.88 \times 10^{-7}\ t^2)$$

Roeser and Wensel (191) give the values shown in Table 6 for the relative resistivity of platinum with a resistivity of 9.83 microhm-cm at 0°C.

In connection with the establishment of the temperature scale between 14° and 83°K, Hoge and Brickwedde (193) determined the resistance of several platinum resistance thermometers over the temperature range 13.96°K to 717.76°K. Averaged values for the rela-

TABLE 6
Relative Electrical Resistivity of Platinum

Temperature ° C.	Ratio R_t/R_o
−200	0.177
−100	0.599
0	1.000
100	1.392
200	1.773
300	2.142
400	2.499
500	2.844
600	3.178
700	3.500
800	3.810
900	4.109
1000	4.396
1100	4.671
1200	4.935
1300	5.187
1400	5.427
1500	5.655

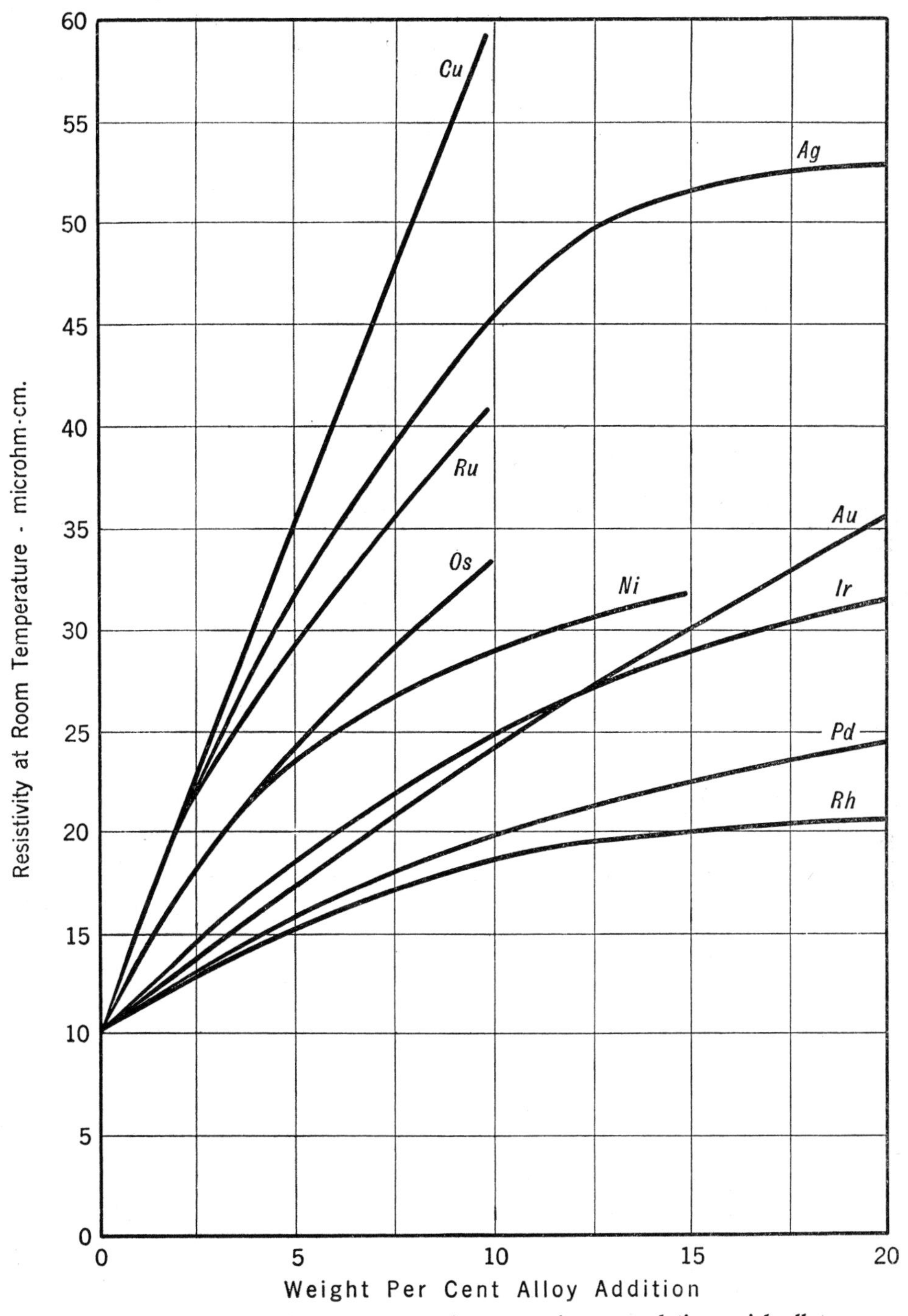

FIG. 4. *Electrical resistivity—concentration curves for some platinum rich alloys.*

tive resistivity on five different high purity platinums studied are shown in Table 7.

TABLE 7
Relative Resistivity of Platinum at Low Temperatures

Temperature ° C.	Temperature ° K	Ratio R_t/R_o ° C.
−259.20	13.96	0.003636
−252.77	20.39	0.006945
−182.97	90.19	0.2459
0	273.16	1.0000
100.00	373.16	1.3914
444.60	717.76	2.6505

Carter (17) using the ratio $\left(\frac{R_t - R_o}{t R_o}\right)$ gives temperature coefficients of 0.003618 per °C over the range 0-500°C, 0.003309 per °C for the range 0-1000°C and 0.002995 per °C for the range 0-1500°C. Other grades of platinum will have somewhat lower coefficients; Grade 4 platinum averaging about 0.0038 per °C over the range 0-100°C.

THERMOELECTRIC FORCE

In the absence of gold as an impurity, the thermal electromotive force of platinum against a standard pure platinum, such as N.B.S. Pt 27, is a sensitive indicator of purity with respect to elements in solid solution. Small amounts of impurities, except gold, make platinum thermoelectrically positive to pure platinum. The thermoelectric force developed between platinum and its platinum rich alloys with other platinum metals and iron are shown in Figure 5 (18). Higher thermoelectric forces are obtained with osmium platinum, iridium platinum and ruthenium platinum than with rhodium platinum but because of the lower volatility and consequent greater stability of the latter, it is preferred for thermocouple elements. The 10% rhodium platinum-pure platinum thermocouple serves to define the International Temperature Scale between 660 and 1063°C but in practise this couple is regularly used at temperatures up to 1300°C and under spe-

TABLE 8
Thermal EMF of Common Metals Relative to Platinum

Temperature ° C.	Tungsten	Molybdenum	Silver	Copper	Gold	Iron	Rhodium	Iridium	Palladium	Nickel	Cobalt
	MILLIVOLTS										
−200	......	......	−0.21	−0.19	−0.21	−3.10	−0.20	−0.25	+0.81	+2.28	......
−100	......	......	−0.39	−0.37	−0.39	−1.94	−0.34	−0.35	+0.48	+1.22	......
0	0	0	0	0	0	0	0	0	0	0	0
+100	+1.12	+1.45	+0.74	+0.76	+0.78	+1.98	+0.70	+0.65	−0.57	−1.48	−1.33
200	2.62	3.19	1.77	1.83	1.84	3.69	1.61	1.49	−1.23	−3.10	−3.08
300	4.48	5.23	3.05	3.15	3.14	5.03	2.68	2.47	−1.99	−4.59	−5.10
400	6.70	7.57	4.57	4.68	4.63	6.08	3.91	3.55	−2.82	−5.45	−7.24
500	9.30	10.20	6.36	6.41	6.29	7.00	5.28	4.78	−3.84	−6.16	−9.35
600	12.56	13.13	8.41	8.34	8.12	8.02	6.77	6.10	−5.03	−7.04	−11.28
700	15.60	16.35	10.75	10.49	10.13	9.34	8.40	7.56	−6.41	−8.10	−12.88
800	19.30	19.87	13.36	12.84	12.29	11.09	10.16	9.12	−7.98	−9.35	−14.00
900	23.36	23.69	16.20	15.41	14.61	13.10	12.04	10.80	−9.72	−10.69	−14.49
1000	27.80	27.80	......	18.20	17.09	14.64	14.05	12.59	−11.63	−12.13	−14.20
1100	32.60	32.21	......	......	......	......	16.18	14.48	−13.70	−13.62	−12.98
1200	37.78	36.91	......	......	......	......	18.42	16.47	−15.89	......	−10.68
1300	......	......	......	......	......	......	20.70	18.47	−18.12	......	......
1400	......	......	......	......	......	......	23.00	20.48	−20.41	......	......
1500	......	......	......	......	......	......	25.35	22.50	−22.74	......	......

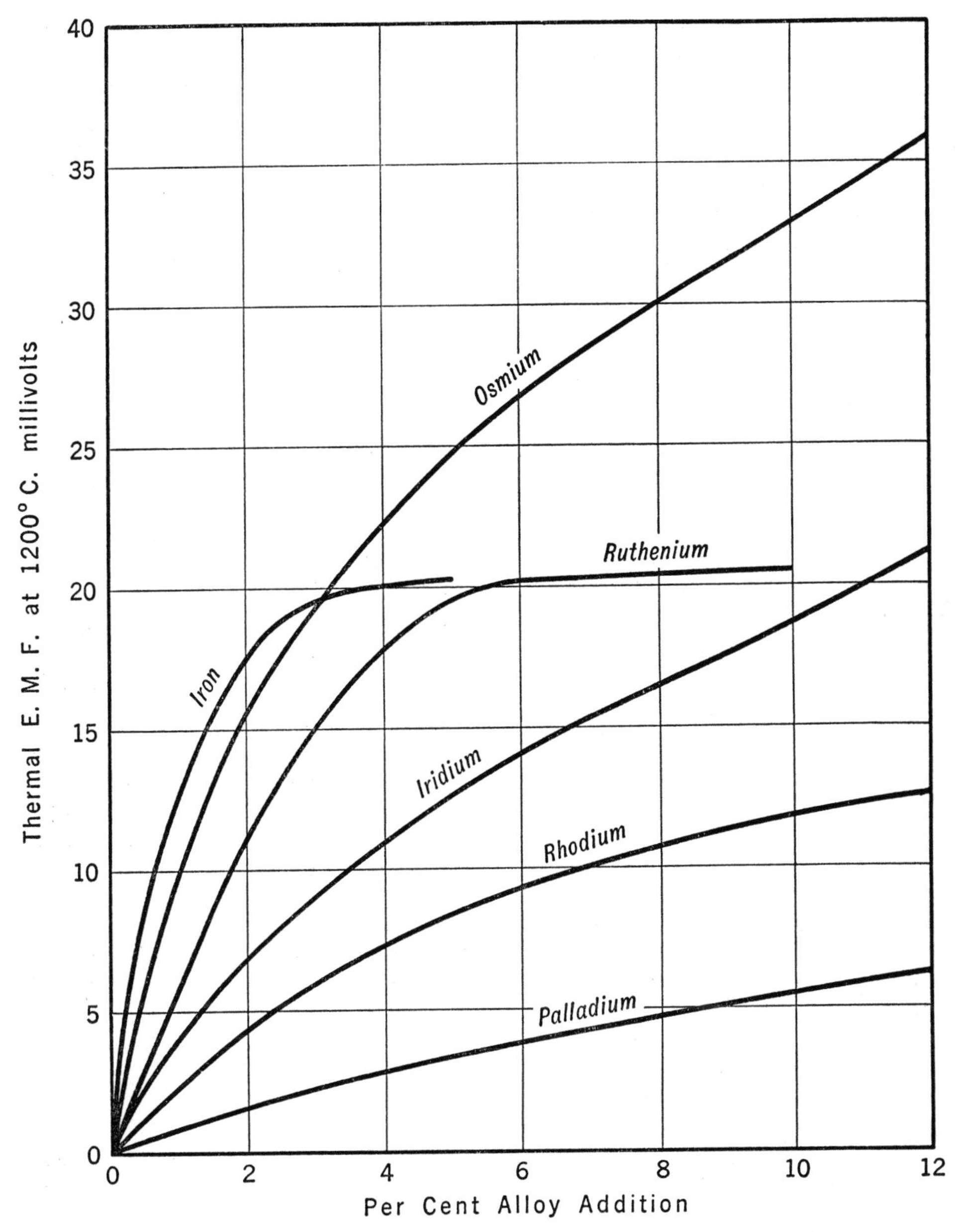

FIG. 5. *Thermal E.M.F. between some platinum rich alloys and pure platinum at 1200°C.*

cial conditions up to 1600°C. Rhenium platinum-pure platinum thermocouples have been proposed as they yield high thermoelectric forces but they lack stability due to loss of rhenium.

The thermoelectric forces developed between pure platinum and a number of other metals, as compiled by Roeser and Wensel (191), are shown in Table 8.

EMISSIVITY Roeser and Wensel (191) give the values shown in Table 9 for the spectral emissivity of platinum and three other platinum metals.

TABLE 9
Spectral Emissivity of Platinum Metals

Metal	E 0.65μ	
	Solid	Liquid
Platinum	0.30	0.38
Palladium	0.33	0.37
Iridium	0.30	....
Rhodium	0.24	0.30

Stephans (192) studied the spectral emissivity of platinum and found it to vary linearly with temperature from 0.283 at 927°C to 0.295 at 1627°C. It should be noted, however, that some other observers (205, 206, 207) found a decrease in spectral emissivity with increase in temperature, while Henning and Heuse (208) found the spectral emissivity to be independent of the temperature.

Greenslade (196) made a comprehensive study of the spectral distribution of energy radiated from metallic surfaces at high temperatures in vacuo. He found that the maximum in the monochromatic emissivity at 1227°C was highest for iron, followed by tungsten, molybdenum, nickel, cobalt, platinum, iridium and rhodium, the radiation from rhodium being slightly less than half that of iron, tungsten, molybdenum or nickel. Unfortunately, total radiation was not measured, but from the curves obtained it is apparent that the total radiation from the platinum metals is much lower than from the other metals noted above.

Values given by Roeser and Wensel (191) for the total emissivity of platinum are shown in Table 10.

TABLE 10
Total Emissivity of Platinum

Temperature ° C.	E_t
25	0.037
100	0.047
500	0.096
1000	0.152
1500	0.191

MAGNETIC SUSCEPTIBILITY Honda and Shimizu (21) found 1.10×10^{-6} mass units for the magnetic susceptibility of annealed platinum at room temperature. They also found cold worked platinum to have a slightly lower susceptibility than annealed platinum. Values for the magnetic susceptibility of platinum and other platinum metals, adapted from the work of Honda (209, 210), are shown in Table 11.

TABLE 11
Specific Magnetic Susceptibility

Temperature ° C.	Platinum	Palladium	Iridium	Rhodium	Ruthenium
	$\lambda \times 10^{-6}$				
18	1.10	5.8	0.15	1.14	0.56
250	.66	4.3	0.18	1.30	.....
500	.55	3.3	0.21	1.46	0.62
750	.44	2.6	0.25	1.55	.....
1000	.36	2.1	0.29	1.80	0.70
1100	.33	1.9	0.30	1.85	0.75

REFLECTIVITY

The specular reflectivity of platinum is higher than that of palladium and lower than that of iridium or rhodium. According to Coblentz (22) the specular reflectivity of platinum is 48% at 0.4 μ, 69% at 0.7 μ and 73% at 1.0 μ. Henning (23) obtained similar values of 62% at 0.52 μ, 65% at 0.576 μ and 68% at

0.68 μ. Auwarter (188) gave slightly lower values of 55% at 0.45 μ, 60% at 0.55 μ, 65% at 0.65 μ and 71% at 0.75 μ. F. L. Jones (24) gave 67.3% as the mean specular reflectivity of electrodeposited platinum with white light.

MECHANICAL PROPERTIES

HARDNESS The Brinell or Vickers hardness of Grade 1 platinum in the annealed condition is about 37, which is slightly above that of pure gold. For the other grades of platinum, the hardness will range from 37 to about 50 BHN or VHN in the annealed condition. Grade 2 platinum averages about 40 BHN or VHN when annealed and Grade 4 platinum, which sometimes requires a rather high annealing temperature to completely soften it, may have a hardness as high as 60 BHN or VHN after a normal short time anneal. Cast platinum usually has a slightly higher hardness than the same grade in the wrought and annealed condition.

Electrodeposited platinum is much harder than wrought platinum according to Atkinson and Raper (25). These investigators, reporting hardness tests made by the National Physical Laboratory with a Vickers type hardness tester using small loads of the order of 20 grams, give 606 to 642 VHN for the hardness of platinum electrodeposited from a complex sodium platinate bath. Hardnesses of electrodeposits from phosphate, sulphate or nitrite ammine baths have not been reported but are believed to be of the same order.

Platinum work hardens at about the same rate as copper or palladium. For Grade 2 platinum, cold rolling increases the Vickers hardness from about 40 VHN, after annealing at 800°C, to 76 VHN after 25% reduction in thickness, to 92 VHN after 50% reduction in thickness and to 108 VHN after 75% reduction in thickness. The rate of hardening (increase in hardness/percent reduction) decreases rapidly up to 30-40% reduction in thickness, gradually increases to 70-80% reduction in thickness and then increases rapidly at higher reductions. Less pure grades of platinum harden slightly more rapidly on cold working.

EFFECT OF ANNEALING ON HARDNESS In addition to purity, the amount of prior cold work, the annealing temperature and the annealing time are important factors affecting the hardness of platinum. Very pure platinum can be annealed at 400°C while Grade 4 platinum may require a temperature as high as 1100°C to completely soften it in a short time. Wise and Vines (187) obtained the annealing curves shown in Figure 6 on a sample of Grade 2 platinum (which was 99.99% Pt) reduced 19 to 89.5% in thickness by cold rolling and annealed for 15 minutes at temperatures up to 1100°C. It will be noted that as the percentage reduction is increased, the temperature necessary for complete softening (complete recrystallization) is lowered. The temperatures required to produce complete softening of this platinum in a 15 minute anneal are approximately 765, 700, 635, 600, 545 and 425°C respectively for reductions in thickness of 19, 39.5, 50.8, 66, 80.5 and 89.5%. In Figure 7, the recrystallization temperature (complete softening), for a 15 minute annealing treatment applied to this platinum, is plotted as

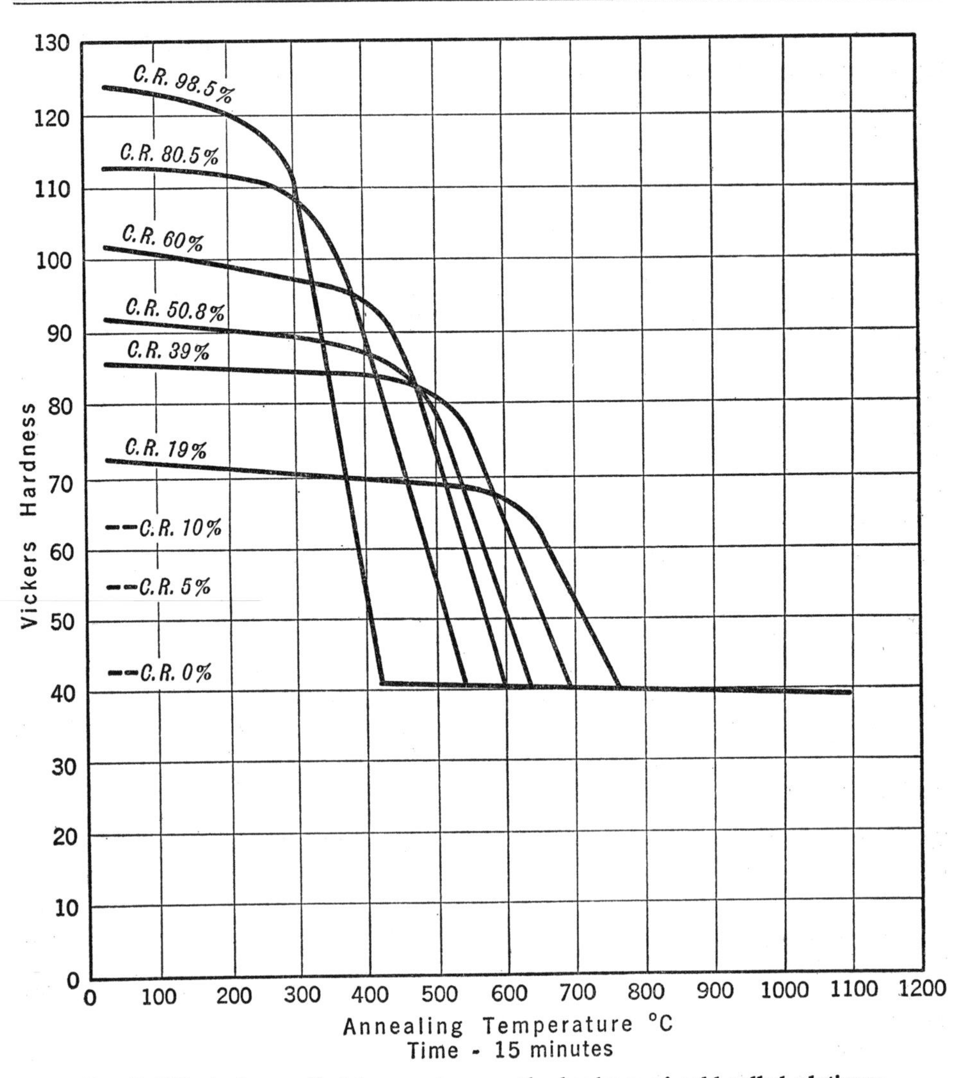

Fig. 6. ***Effect of annealing temperature on the hardness of cold rolled platinum.***

a function of the percentage cold reduction and the cold worked hardness. From this curve the marked effect of cold work in reducing the recrystallization temperature is obvious. Increasing the annealing time lowers the recrystallization temperature, but once the sample has completely recrystallized, the hardness is not materially lowered by increasing the time or temperature of annealing. Other grades of platinum will, of course, have different annealing characteristics; less pure grades requiring higher annealing temperatures.

In the sample of Grade 2 platinum studied by Wise and Vines (187), the recrystallized grain size was found to be dependent upon the percentage cold reduction which governs the recrystallization temperature; i.e., the higher the percentage cold reduction the lower the temperature necessary for recrystallization and the smaller the resultant grain

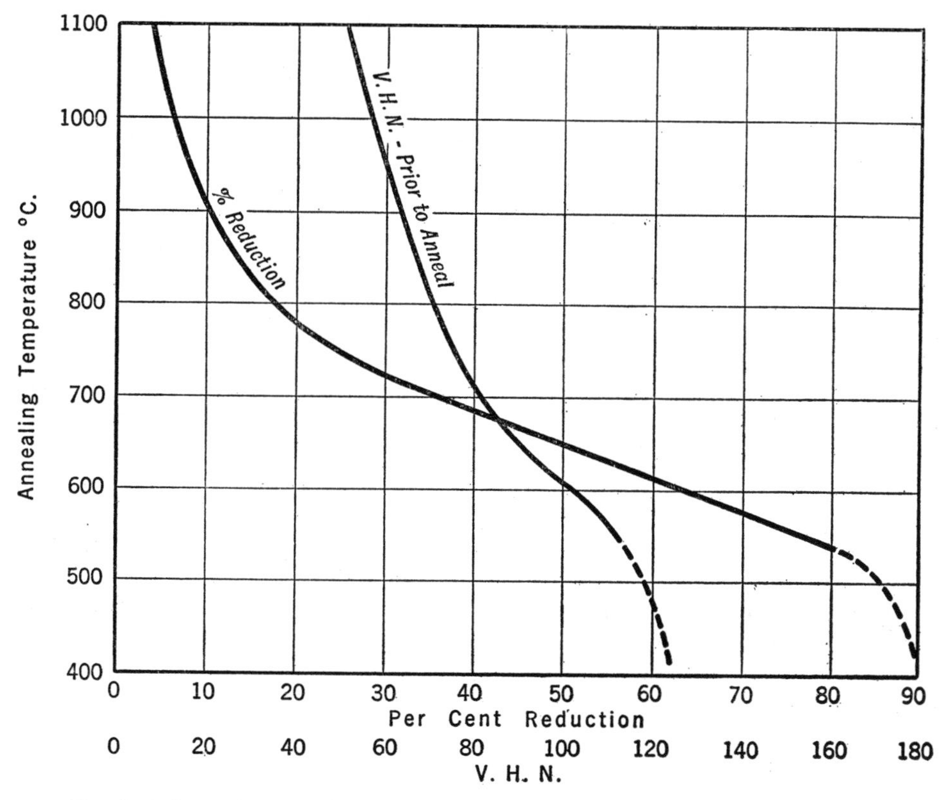

FIG. 7. *Relation between the percentage cold reduction or the cold rolled hardness of pure platinum and the temperature required to produce full softening in 15 minutes.*

size. The grain size of this sample of platinum was not materially affected by increasing the time or temperature of annealing. Similar lack of grain growth has been observed in other samples of platinum by other investigators but the grain size of some platinum samples is markedly increased by high temperature treatments. The reason for this difference in behavior of substantially pure platinums has not been determined.

EFFECT OF ALLOYING ELEMENTS ON HARDNESS

The hardening effect of alloying additions upon platinum is shown graphically in Figure 8. Of these metals, nickel produces the greatest hardening per unit weight and palladium the least. Of the platinum metals, osmium is the most potent hardener followed by ruthenium, iridium, rhodium and palladium. Although osmium and ruthenium are more effective hardeners per unit weight than iridium, the latter is the preferred hardener for platinum in the United States primarily because of its development in jewelry. The volatility of osmium, the toxicity of osmic oxide and the difficulty of working the high osmium alloys discourages the use of this metal as a hardening agent except in special cases. Ruthenium appears to be a satisfactory hardener and the 5% alloy finds use for jewelry and the 10% alloy for magneto contacts. Although they are not accepted in the United States, the 3.0 and 4.5% copper plat-

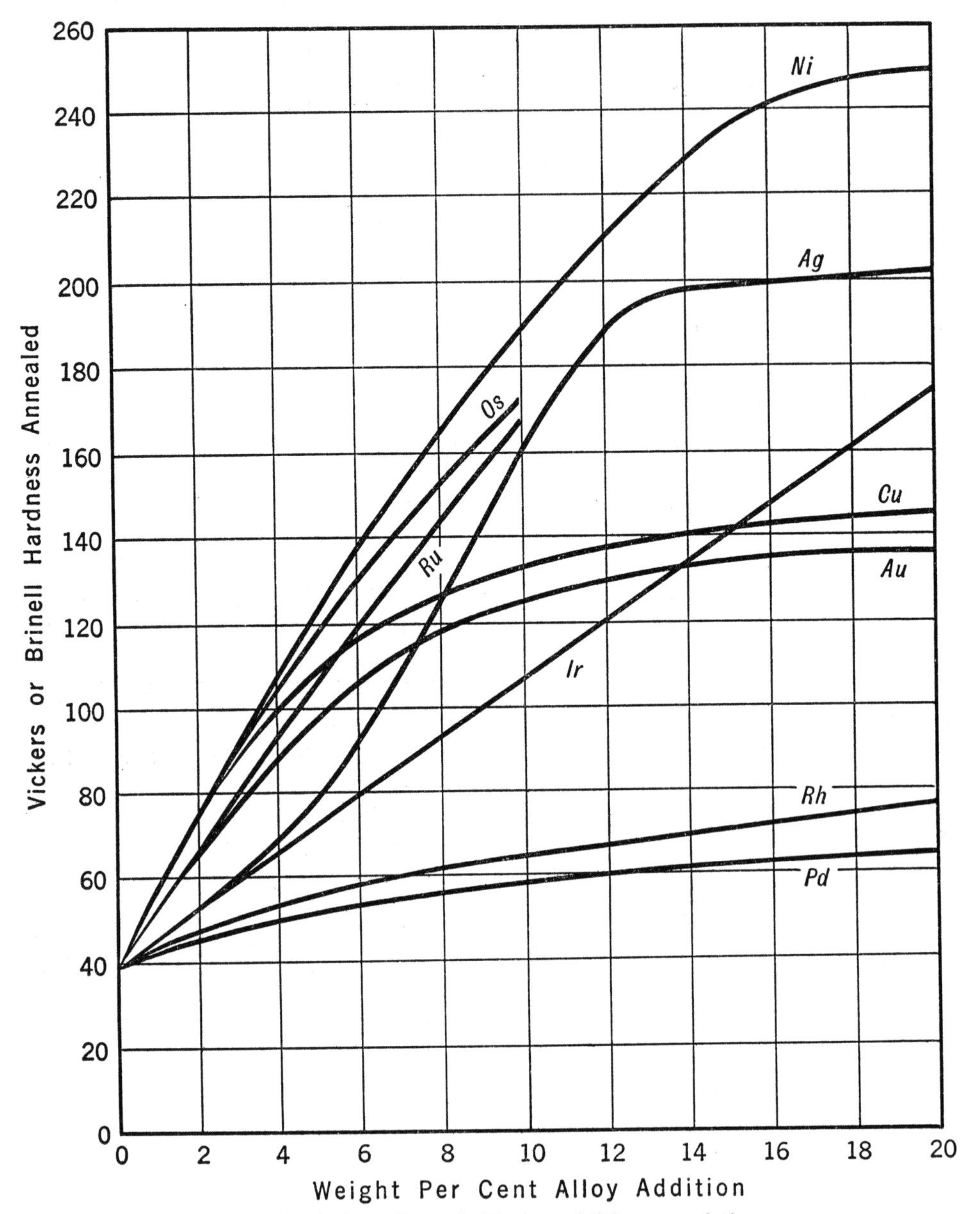

FIG. 8. ***Hardening effect of alloying additions on platinum.***

inum alloys have been used for jewelry purposes in certain European countries.

TENSILE STRENGTH The tensile strength of platinum is markedly dependent upon the amount and nature of the minor impurities present and even for one grade a range of values is obtained. According to Sivil (26) the tensile strength in the annealed condition averages about 18,000 lbs. per sq. in. for Grade 1 platinum and about 20,000 lbs. per. sq. in. for Grade 2 platinum. Wise and

TABLE 12
Tensile Strengths of Platinum Alloys at Room Temperature and at 1000°C
(Samples previously annealed at 1100°C)

Composition	Tensile Strength Lbs. per sq. in.		Strength Ratio
	Room Temperature	1000 ° C.	Strength 1000 ° C. / Strength R. T.
Grade 2 Platinum	20,700	4,080	.197
Grade 4 Platinum	23,500	5,190	.221
5% Iridium Platinum	39,200	9,290	.237
5% Nickel Platinum	62,800	15,700	.25
10% Rhodium Platinum	47,900	13,600	.286
5% Rhodium, 20% Palladium Platinum	52,600	11,800	.225

Eash (27) found the tensile strength of Grade 2 platinum produced in 1934 to be 22,000 lbs. per sq. in. in the annealed condition and 36,000 lbs. per sq. in. when cold drawn to 50% reduction in area. In recent tests on a sample of Grade 2 platinum, values of 19,350 lbs. per sq. in. in the annealed condition and 29,500 lbs. per sq. in. when cold swaged 50% were obtained. For Grade 4 platinum the tensile strength may be as high as 30,000 lbs. per sq. in. when annealed and 50,000 lbs. per sq. in. when cold rolled 50%.

TENSILE STRENGTHS AT HIGH TEMPERATURES (28) The tensile strength of previously annealed Grade 2 platinum falls smoothly from 20,700 lbs. per sq. in. at room temperature to 3,400 lbs. per sq. in. at 1100°C. A Grade 4 platinum had somewhat higher tensile strengths throughout this temperature range, but at 1100°C the tensile strength closely approached that of Grade 2 platinum. The tensile strengths of various alloys of platinum, previously annealed at 1100°C, at room temperature and at 1000°C are given in Table 12.

Of the alloys tested, the 5% nickel platinum has the highest tensile strength at 1000°C but the tensile strength of this alloy on increasing temperature falls faster than that of the 10% rhodium alloy and at temperatures above 1100°C the latter alloy is stronger than the 5% nickel platinum. Stauss (29) concluded, from the results of tensile tests on fine wires of platinum alloys at temperatures up to 1600°C, that alloys which are simple solid solutions retain equal fractions of their strengths at equal fractions of their melting points, and that a higher melting alloy maintains its strength better than a lower melting one.

EFFECT OF ALLOYING ELEMENTS ON TENSILE STRENGTH In general, the effect of alloying additions on the tensile strength parallels the effect on hardness shown in Figure 8. The tensile strengths of various platinum alloys in the cold worked (50% reduction in area) and annealed (5-30 minutes) conditions are given in Table 13.

PROPORTIONAL LIMIT Pure platinum has a very low proportional limit in the annealed state. Values between 2,000 and 5,500 lbs. per sq. in. when annealed, and about 27,000 lbs. per sq. in. when cold worked 50%, have been reported for the proportional limit of Grade 2 platinum. Due to the strengthening effect of impurities, other grades of platinum have higher proportional limits.

TABLE 13
Tensile Strengths of Platinum Alloys

Alloy	Tensile Strength Cold Worked 50% Reduction Lbs. per sq. in.	Annealing Temp. ° C.	Tensile Strength Annealed Lbs. per sq. in.
Grade 1 Platinum	28,000–30,000	900	18,000
Grade 2 Platinum	30,000–36,000	1000	18,000–22,000
Grade 4 Platinum	36,000–50,000	1100	22,000–30,000
5% Iridium Platinum	69,000	1200	39,000
10% Iridium Platinum	82,200	1200	53,000
20% Iridium Platinum	140,500	1400	93,000
10% Rhodium Platinum	84,300	1200	47,000
5% Nickel Platinum	103,000	1000	65,000
5% Rhodium, 20% Palladium Platinum	85,000	1100	53,000
10% Ruthenium Platinum	137,000	1200	85,000
4.5% Copper Platinum	82,500	1000	55,000
5% Gold Platinum	63,500	1000	45,500
10% Gold Platinum	90,000	1000	77,500

EFFECT OF ALLOYING ADDITIONS ON THE PROPORTIONAL LIMIT Even small amounts of alloying additions markedly increase the proportional limit in the annealed state. In general, the relative effect of alloying additions to platinum on the proportional limit is about the same as their effect on tensile strength. Values for the proportional limit of several platinum alloys in the cold worked (50% reduction) and annealed (5-30 minutes) conditions are given in Table 14.

ELONGATION The percentage elongation of platinum does not change markedly from grade to grade and ranges from about 2.5 to 3.5% in 2 inches for the cold worked (50% reduction) state and from about 30 to 40% in 2 inches for the annealed condition.

YOUNG'S MODULUS Wegel (30) recently determined the Young's Modulus of platinum and found it to be 21,300,000 lbs. per sq. in. when annealed and 22,600,000 lbs. per sq. in. when hard rolled.

TABLE 14
Proportional Limits of Platinum Alloys

Alloy	Proportional Limit Cold Worked 50% Reduction Lbs. per sq. in.	Annealing Temperature ° C.	Proportional Limit Annealed Lbs. per sq. in.
Grade 1 Platinum	......	900	<2,000
Grade 2 Platinum	27,000	1000	2,000–5,500
Grade 4 Platinum	27,000	1100	3,000–6,500
5% Iridium Platinum	53,500	1200	18,000
10% Iridium Platinum	54,000	1200	30,000
20% Iridium Platinum	100,900	1400	59,000
10% Rhodium Platinum	55,600	1200	17,000
5% Nickel Platinum	70,000	1000	33,000
5% Rhodium, 20% Palladium Platinum	51,900	1100	17,000
4.5% Copper Platinum	54,500	1050	12,000
5% Gold Platinum	40,500	1000	13,000
10% Gold Platinum	63,500	1000	46,000

WORKING TECHNOLOGY (31)

Platinum is very ductile and can be worked hot or cold. To secure more rapid reduction, it is usual to begin hot working ingots at temperatures of about 1000°C, for as much as 50% reduction in thickness can be obtained in one pass at this temperature. Cold work on sheets is done in steps of about 10% reduction per pass with intermediate anneals after about 75% reduction in thickness. Wire is cold rolled or swaged and then drawn through tungsten carbide or diamond dies, the reduction or draft depending upon the size.

Platinum withstands drastic cold working and can be beaten into thin leaf or foil in the same manner as gold. It may also be drawn bare into wire as small as .0004″ in diameter and by the Wollaston method, with a silver jacket, wire as small as .00005″ in diameter can be produced. Most platinum rich alloys receive similar treatment although reductions are not as great and swaging is preferred to drawing for working wire of the harder alloys.

Platinum responds well to the usual cold forming operations except that it is somewhat difficult to work in a punch press or turn in a lathe as it drags instead of cutting, presumably because lubricants do not react with it. Generally speaking, the alloys behave much better in this respect.

Grade 2 platinum can be annealed to maximum ductility at about 600-700°C but other less pure grades require higher annealing temperatures; 1200°C being necessary to thoroughly anneal Grade 4 platinum in a short time. Platinum alloys containing considerable percentages of osmium, ruthenium, or iridium require even higher annealing temperatures for short time anneals.

Platinum is best annealed in air but other atmospheres may be employed without damage. However, care should be taken to prevent contact with compounds of silicon, phosphorus, lead, bismuth or other easily reducible elements if a reducing atmosphere is used. It is also advisable to pickle platinum before annealing to remove iron and other contaminants picked up during working.

Platinum is easily hammer welded by gently hammering at about 1000°C. It can also be soldered with fine gold or a white platinum solder and can be arc or flame and spot or seam resistance welded.

USES

The many diverse uses of the alloyed platinums are listed separately in the review of the platinum alloy systems beginning on page 56.

In the unalloyed form, platinum is used for catalysts, thermocouple and resistance thermometer elements, electrical contacts, crucibles and laboratory ware, dental foil, safety disks, electrodes, heat and corrosion resistant equipment and for jewelry. In the form of platinum clad base metal, there is an expanding field of application for processing equipment in the chemical industry.

CATALYSTS In the production of sulphuric acid by the oxidation of sulphur dioxide, the ability of finely divided platinum to adsorb gases and promote oxidation accounts for its wide use as a catalyst in this process.

Pure platinum can be employed in the oxidation of ammonia for the production of nitric acid, but the 5% or 10% rhodium platinum alloy is preferred for this purpose.

Platinum is also an excellent hydrogenation catalyst and is used in the laboratory for the hydrogenation of special organic compounds. Platinum is also the catalyst employed in igniters of flameless cigarette lighters and automatic gas lighters; in devices for analyzing and detecting combustible gases, and in flameless, benzine-burning, low temperature hand warmers.

MEASURING EQUIPMENT The platinum resistance thermometer and the rhodium platinum-platinum thermocouple are used to define the International Temperature Scale between −190°C and 660°C and 660°C and 1063°C respectively. Recently the platinum resistance thermometer was employed to establish the temperature scale between −259°C and −190°C. In practise, the platinum resistance thermometer is used for measuring temperatures up to 800 or 900°C while the rhodium platinum-platinum thermocouple is regularly employed at temperatures up to 1300°C and under special conditions as high as 1600°C. The International Light Standard is based on the radiation from a black body at the freezing point of platinum.

ELECTRICAL Electrical contacts which must give dependable service and possess very low contact resistance at low contact pressures are made of platinum, palladium or platinum metal alloys. Fuses to protect delicate electrical instruments are made of extremely fine platinum wire. For temperature compensators platinum wire is also used due to its high and reproducible temperature coefficient of resistance.

CHEMICAL Corrosion resisting safety or blow-out disks of platinum are used for protecting pressure vessels handling corrosive materials, particularly those containing fluorine compounds. Platinum electrodes are used for the electrolytic production of hydrogen peroxide and "per-salts" because they have a high oxygen over voltage and do not corrode or affect the purity of the product. In various other electrochemical processes, platinum is used extensively as an insoluble anode.

Pure platinum, as well as platinum containing small amounts of rhodium or iridium, is used for crucibles and other laboratory ware.

In the production of large synthetic crystals of lithium fluoride and other transparent media for optical purposes, platinum is used as the crucible which must hold the molten mass for long periods without contamination.

Platinum clad nickel, copper, silver or various alloys are used in the chemical industry in the form of sheet, rod, wire and tubing from which all types of chemical equipment are constructed, such as heating and cooling coils, bayonet and candle heaters, evaporators, stills and autoclaves.

DENTAL Because platinum and its alloys will withstand the high firing temperature without distorting or discoloring porcelain, they are used for making porcelain jacketed crowns for dental restorations and as structural bases for certain types of fixed or removable porcelain bridge work. The bridge frames are either soldered together from wrought sections or cast in one piece. Porcelain coated cast platinum or platinum alloy inlays are a recent development in this field.

GLASS PRODUCTS Platinum, rhodium platinum or other high platinum alloys are used in large quantities in feeding mechanisms of glass working equipment to resist attack by molten glass, prevent contamination of the product and insure constancy of the orifice dimensions which fix the size of the glass products. This use has made possible the commercial development of glass fiber and wool and permitted economies in the production of glass insulators used for the bases of electric light bulbs.

JEWELRY Some jewelry is made of pure platinum, but most frequently, the harder and stronger iridium-platinum and ruthenium-platinum alloys are employed in this field.

DECORATIVE ARTS "Liquid platinum" applied as a varnish and reduced to metal by firing is applied on glass and china ware for obtaining metallic decorative effects. Platinum leaf, made by beating in a manner similar to that employed in producing gold leaf, is used for decorative effects in architecture and also for stamping tooled leather book bindings. Platinotype photographic printing paper, which yields richer toned, more permanent photographs than silver papers, is made by treating the paper with salts of iron and platinum.

PALLADIUM

Palladium resembles platinum in many respects and follows it in importance and abundance. It is the end member of the second series of transition elements with an atomic number of 46 and an atomic weight of 106.7.

DENSITY Palladium is the lightest metal of the platinum group and has a density of 11.96 gms/cm^3 at 18°C or about 56% that of platinum. Owen and Yates (3) calculated the density from the space lattice as 12.02 gms/cm^3 at 20°C.

LATTICE Palladium has a face centered cubic structure with a lattic parameter of 3.8825 ± .0003A at 20°C according to Owen and Jones (195).

ALLOTROPY It is now believed that palladium suffers no allotropic transformation between 0°C and the melting point as, although Jaeger and Rosenbohm (32) found a maximum in the specific heat-temperature curve at 1520°C, this was not evident in the later more exact work of Jaeger and Veenstra (33). It should be mentioned, however, that Jaeger and Zanstra (34) reported changes in the X-ray diffraction pattern of palladium at 1200°C but this is not believed to be indicative of allotropic changes.

THERMAL PROPERTIES

MELTING POINT The melting point of palladium as determined from the brightness ratios of freezing gold and palladium is 1554.4 ± 1°C according to Schofield (35) and 1553.6 ± 0.5°C according to Fairchild, Hoover and Peters (36). Morris and Scholes (37) gave 1555°C. The value 1554°C is accordingly selected as the melting point of palladium and is lowest of the platinum metals.

BOILING POINT Richardson (38) estimated the boiling point of palladium as 3980°C and Mott (39) as 3000°C. Richardson's value may be somewhat high but Mott's value is believed to be too low. Both of these estimates were based on arc methods but that employed by Richardson, the later investigator, was more refined and accordingly should be given more weight.

VAPOR PRESSURE From the estimated boiling points, it is believed that palladium has the highest vapor pressure of the platinum metals but reliable data are not available. Comparative tests in air and vacuo show that the loss in weight of palladium at high temperatures is due to the volatilization of the metal, per se, while with the other platinum metals the higher loss of weight in air indicates that this loss is due to the oxidation of the metal and volatilization of the oxide formed. At 1300°C, in air, the volatility of palladium is six times that of rhodium, three times that of platinum and one-tenth that of iridium according to Crookes (8).

THERMAL CONDUCTIVITY The thermal conductivity of palladium is 0.161 cal/sec. cm^2 °C/cm at 0°C, 0.168 at 18°C and 0.177 at 100°C according to Jaeger and Diesselhorst (11).

THERMAL EXPANSION Holborn and Day (13) gave 11.67 x 10^{-6} for the coefficient of linear expansion of palladium at 0°C. They also established the relation:

$$l_t = l_0 (1 + 1.167 \times 10^{-5}t + 2.187 \times 10^{-9}t^2)$$

for the range 0-1000°C. Holzmann (40) gave the relation $l_t = l_{20} [1 + 1.0637 \times 10^{-5} (t-20) + 4.594 \times 10^{-9} (t-20)^2 - 1.521 \times 10^{-12} (t-20)^3]$ for the range 20—1000°C. Values computed from the above relations, assuming unit length at 0°C and comparable lengths at 20°C, are given in Table 15 from which it will be observed that these relations give similar expansion curves:

TABLE 15
Thermal Expansion of Palladium

Temperature °C.	Holborn and Day L_t/L_o	Holzmann L_t/L_o
0	1.000000	1.000000
20	1.000234	1.000234
100	1.00119	1.00111
200	1.00242	1.00228
300	1.0037	1.0035
400	1.0050	1.0048
500	1.0064	1.0062
600	1.0078	1.0076
700	1.0092	1.0091
800	1.0107	1.0106
900	1.0123	1.0121
1000	1.0139	1.0136

Thermal expansion curves for palladium and other platinum metals are shown in Figure 1.

SPECIFIC HEAT Values between 0.0537 and 0.0584 cal/gm at 0°C have been reported for the true specific heat of palladium. The most recent determination, that of Jaeger and Veenstra (33) is 0.058378 cal/gm at 0.°C. These investigators also give the relation $c_p = 0.058378 + 1.20548 \times 10^{-5}t + 2.58 \times 10^{-10}t^2$ for the true specific heat at temperatures up to the melting point. Holzmann (40) gave the relation

$$c_p = 0.05841 + 1.5853 \times 10^{-5}t$$

for temperatures up to 1000°C. Values computed from the above relations are given in Table 16. In Figure 2, the specific heats of palladium and the other platinum metals are shown graphically.

TABLE 16
Specific Heat of Palladium

Temperature °C.	Specific Heat cal/gm	
	Jaeger and Veenstra	Holzmann
0	0.058378	0.05841
100	0.0596	0.0600
200	0.0608	0.0616
300	0.0620	0.0632
400	0.0632	0.0647
500	0.0644	0.0663
600	0.0657	0.0679
700	0.0669	0.0695
800	0.0682	0.0711
900	0.0694	0.0727
1000	0.0707	0.0743
1100	0.0719	......
1200	0.0732	......
1300	0.0745	......
1400	0.0757	......
1500	0.0770	......

ELECTRICAL

The average of the more recent values reported for the electrical resistivity of annealed palladium is 10.8 microhm-cm at 20°C. From this value and the temperature coefficient, the electrical resistivity at 0° and 100°C are calculated as 10.0 and 13.8 microhm-cm respectively. Grube and Knabe (41),

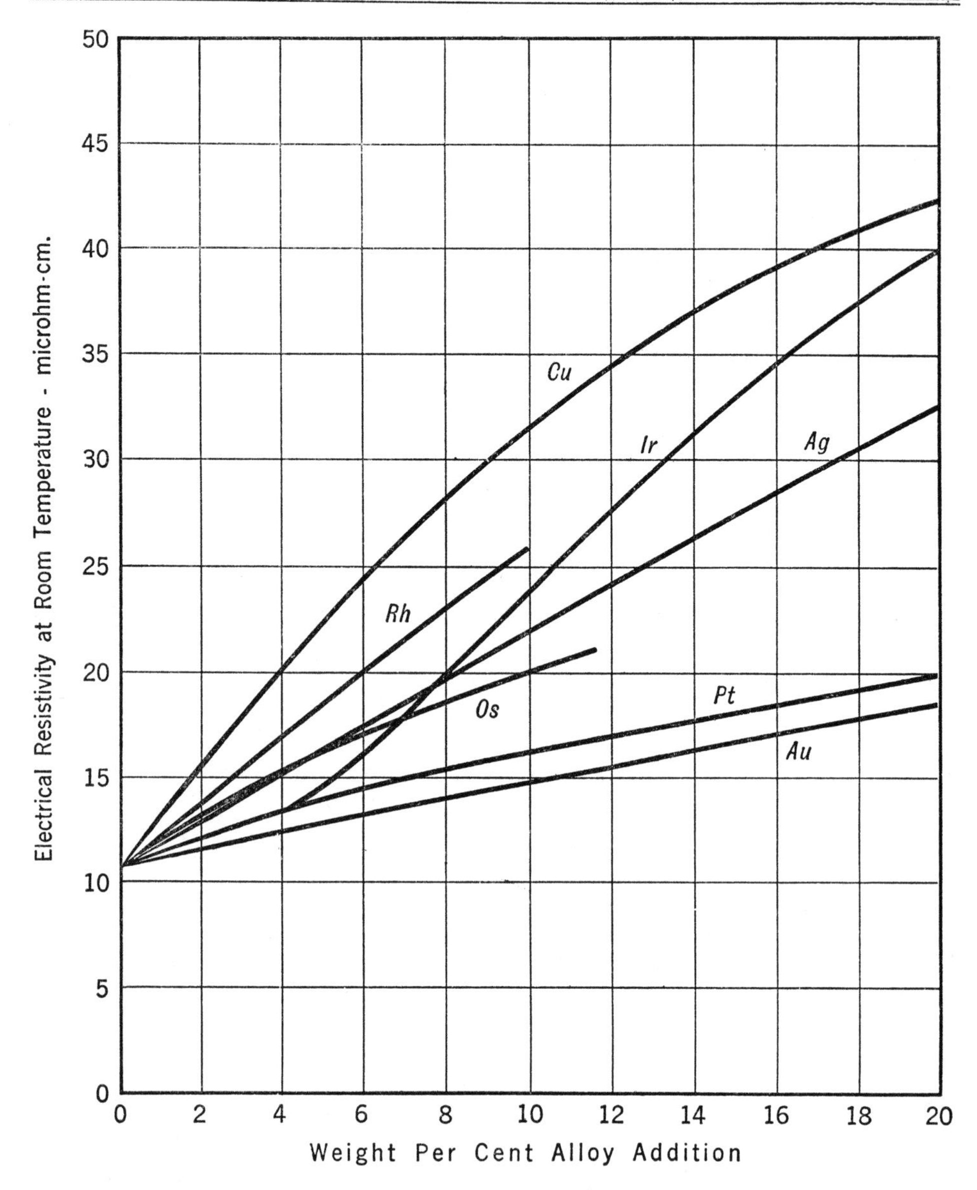

FIG. 9. *Electrical resistivity—concentration curves for some palladium rich alloys.*

Grube and Kastner (42) and Connybeare (43) determined the electrical resistivity of palladium at higher temperatures. Their results, which are in fair agreement, are given in Table 17. Connybeare (43) reports that lengthy annealing treatments in the neighborhood of 1000°C increases the resistivity of palladium, which he presumes to be due to the development of intercrystalline fissures. Thus the resistivity of palladium at 0°C was 10.63 microhm-cm after annealing at 650°C and increased to 12.38 microhm-cm after annealing at 970°-1000°C for three days.

TABLE 17
Electrical Resistivity of Palladium

Temperature ° C.	Resistivity Microhm-cm		
	Grube and Knabe	Grube and Kastner	Connybeare
0	....	......	10.63
100	14.0	14.3	14.6
200	17.4	17.4	18.4
300	21.0	20.7	22.1
400	24.3	23.8	25.5
500	27.4	26.8	28.7
600	30.4	29.9	31.6
700	33.2	32.6	34.2
800	35.6	35.2	36.7
900	37.9	37.7	....
1000	40.0	40.0	....
1200	44.8	....	....
1400	49.5	....	....

EFFECT OF ALLOYING ADDITIONS ON RESISTIVITY

The effect of additions of other metals to palladium on the electrical resistivity is shown graphically in Figure 9. Of these metals, copper produces the greatest increase per unit weight and gold the least.

TEMPERATURE COEFFICIENT OF ELECTRICAL RESISTANCE

The temperature coefficient of electrical resistance $\left(\frac{R_{100} - R_0}{100\ R_0}\right)$ of annealed palladium is between 0.0037 and 0.0038 per degree C, the best value being about 0.00377 per degree C. According to Schofield (44) this value is dependent upon the temperature used for annealing the palladium. He gave 0.00371 for wire annealed at 1100°C and 0.00380 for that annealed near the melting point. On the other hand Connybeare (43) gave 0.00372 for wire annealed at 650°C and 0.00370 for wire annealed at about 1000°C for 3 days. In Table 18 are given the values for the ratio R_t/R_0 obtained by Connybeare (43) on palladium annealed at 650°C.

TABLE 18
Relative Resistivity of Palladium

Temperature ° C.	Ratio R_t/R_0
−183.	0.2283
−103.9	0.5788
− 78.6	0.6840
0	1.000
100	1.372
200	1.730
300	2.078
400	2.395
500	2.704
600	2.972
700	3.220
800	3.449

For the ratio $\left(\frac{R_t - R_0}{t\ R_0}\right)$ Holborn (45) gave 0.00377 per degree C over the range 0°–100°C, 0.00364 for the range 0°–200°C, 0.00353 for the range 0°–300°C and 0.00345 for the range 0°–400°C. Carter (17) gave 0.00236 for this ratio over the range 0–1200°C.

THERMOELECTRIC FORCE

Palladium is the only metal of the platinum group which is thermoelectrically negative to platinum. The thermoelectric force of a palladium-platinum couple with a cold junction at 0°C is given in Table 19. (20)

TABLE 19
Thermal EMF of a Palladium-Platinum Couple

Temperature ° C.	EMF Millivolts
−185	+ 0.77
− 80	+ 0.39
0	0
100	− 0.57
300	− 1.99
500	− 3.84
700	− 6.41
900	− 9.72
1100	−13.70
1300	−18.12
1500	−22.74

MAGNETIC SUSCEPTIBILITY The magnetic susceptibility of palladium at room temperature is 5.20×10^{-6} mass units according to Shimizu (46). Honda (47) gave 5.8×10^{-6} mass units. Values for the magnetic susceptibility at high temperatures are given on page 24.

REFLECTIVITY

The specular reflectivity of palladium is slightly lower than that of platinum. According to von Wartenberg (48) it is 65% at 0.579 μ. Auwarter (188) reports the specular reflectivity as 54%, 60%, 63% and 66% at 0.45, 0.55, 0.65 and 0.75 μ, respectively. Jones (24) gives 62.8% for the mean specular reflectivity of electro deposited palladium with white light. Kenworthy (49) reports 57 to 59% for electrodeposited palladium.

MECHANICAL PROPERTIES

HARDNESS Annealed pure palladium has about the same hardness as annealed pure platinum, the Vickers hardness being 37 VHN after annealing at 800°C. Commercial palladium has an average Vickers or Brinell hardness of about 46 after annealing at 800°C and about 44 after annealing at 1000 or 1100°C. The Brinell hardness of cast commercial palladium is about 49 BHN.

The hardnesses of palladium electroplates have been measured by the National Physical Laboratory using a diamond pyramidal indenter similar to the Vickers but with a very small load of about 20 grams. Palladium electroplate deposited from the palladosamine bath has a hardness of 190-196 VHN while that deposited from a complex alkali metal nitrite bath containing chlorides has a hardness of 387-435 VHN (50).

Commercial palladium work hardens about the same amount as platinum, the Vickers hardness increasing from 44 VHN, for palladium annealed at 1100°C, to 88 VHN after a reduction in thickness of 25% by cold rolling and to 106 VHN after a reduction in thickness of 50%.

EFFECT OF ALLOYING ADDITIONS ON HARDNESS The hardening effect of alloying additions of other metals to palladium is shown graphically in Figure 10. Of these metals, ruthenium produces the greatest hardening per unit weight and platinum the least. Of the platinum metals, ruthenium is the most potent hardener followed by iridium, osmium, rhodium and platinum. Nickel is also an effective hardener for palladium. Ruthenium is the preferred hardener for palladium in this country although rhodium is usually added with it.

TENSILE STRENGTH The tensile strength of pure palladium annealed at 900°C for one-half hour is 27,500 lbs. per sq. in. according to Carter (51). Wise and Eash (27) found the tensile strength of commercial palladium to be 30,000 lbs. per sq. in. when annealed at 800 or 900°C for 5 minutes and 47,000 lbs. per sq. in. when reduced 50% in area by cold drawing. The effect of annealing temperature on the tensile properties of commercial palladium is shown in Figure 11.

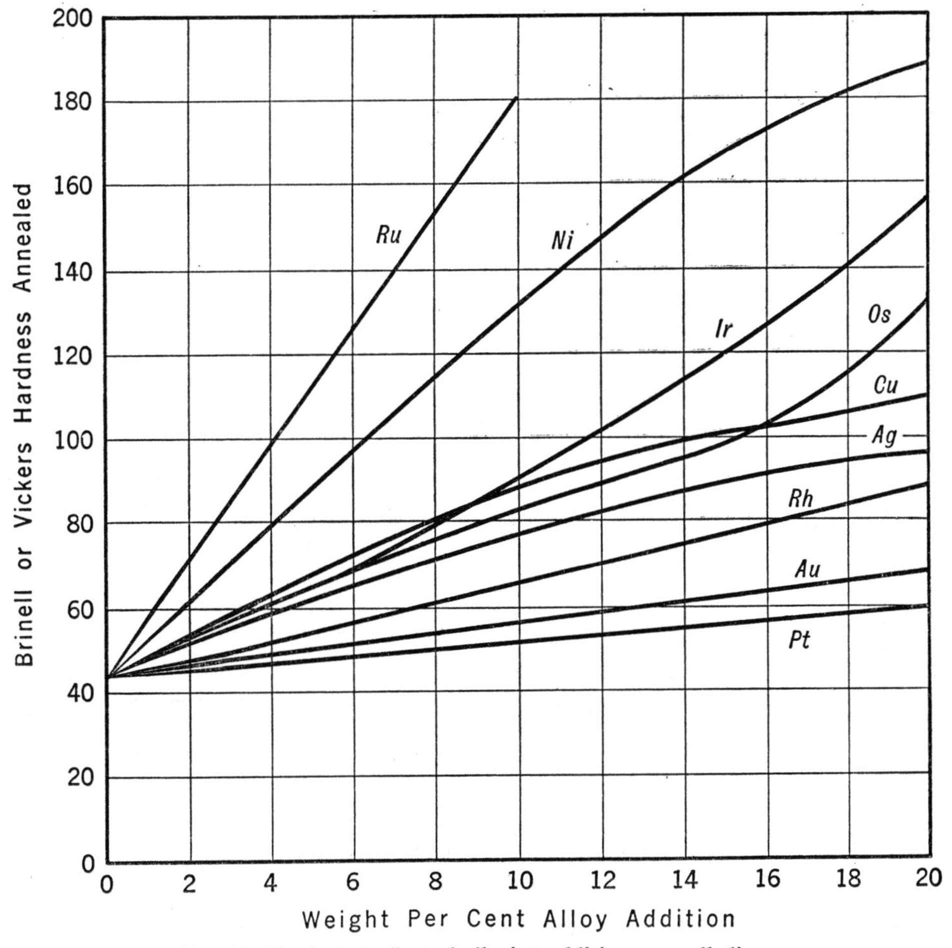

FIG. 10. ***Hardening effect of alloying additions on palladium.***

EFFECT OF TEMPERATURE (28) The tensile strength of commercial palladium, previously annealed at 1100°C, falls smoothly from about 28,000 lbs. per sq. in. at room temperature to 2,920 lbs. per sq. in. at 1100°C. The tensile strengths of palladium and a 1% rhodium, 4% ruthenium palladium alloy at intermediate temperatures are shown in Table 20.

EFFECT OF ALLOYING ADDITIONS ON TENSILE STRENGTH Generally, the effect of alloying additions on the tensile strength parallels the effect on hardness which is shown in Figure 10. The tensile

TABLE 20
Tensile Strength of Commercial Palladium and a Palladium Jewelry Alloy at Temperatures up to 1100°C
Samples previously annealed at 1100°C

Temperature °C.	Tensile Strength Lbs. per sq. in	
	Commercial Palladium	1% Rh 4% Ru 95% Pd
Room	28,000	55,200
200	24,500	45,300
400	18,100	36,900
600	12,700	26,000
800	8,300	15,300
1000	3,820	7,480
1100	2,920	5,500

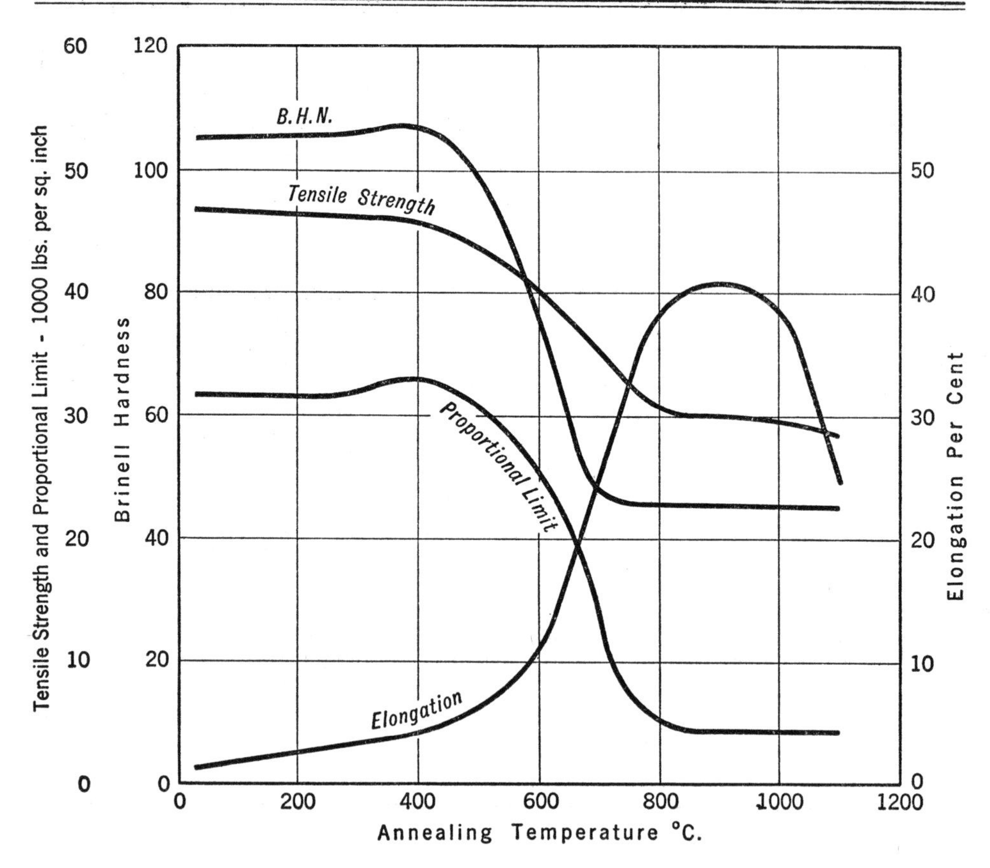

FIG. 11. *Effect of annealing temperature on the tensile properties and hardness of hard drawn palladium.*

TABLE 21
Tensile Strength of Palladium Alloys

Alloy	Tensile Strength Cold Worked (50% Reduction) Lbs. per sq. in.	Annealing Temperature ° C.	Tensile Strength Annealed Lbs. per sq. in.
Commercial Palladium..................	47,000	800	30,000
10% Gold Palladium..................	57,000*	800	34,000
10% Silver Palladium..................	75,000*	800	39,000
3% Rhodium, 2% Ruthenium Palladium..	61,000	1000	45,800
1% Rhodium, 4% Ruthenium Palladium..	71,500	1000	58,000
5.5% Rhodium, 4.5% Ruthenium Palladium	82,000	1000	61,500
3% Ruthenium Palladium...............	85,000	1200	54,000

*66% reduction in area.

strengths of several palladium alloys in the cold worked (50% reduction) and annealed conditions are given in Table 21.

PROPORTIONAL LIMIT Annealed pure palladium has a very low proportional limit. Wise and Eash (27) found the proportional limit of commercial palladium to be about 5,000 lbs. per sq. in. after annealing at 800°C and 30,000 lbs. per sq. in. after a reduction of 50% in area by cold drawing. Table 22 gives the proportional limit of a few important palladium alloys.

ELONGATION The elongation of palladium drops from 40% in 2" for wire annealed at 800 or 900°C to 24% in 2" for wire annealed at 1100°C. It is 1.5% in 2" after a reduction of 50% in area by cold drawing. In Figure 11 the effect of annealing temperature on the elongation is shown graphically.

YOUNG'S MODULUS Young's modulus of annealed palladium is 16,000,000 lbs. per sq. in. according to Schaffer (52) and 16,300,000 lbs. per sq. in. according to Gruneisen (53).

TABLE 22
Proportional Limit of Palladium Alloys

Alloy	Proportional Limit Cold Worked (50% Reduction) Lbs. per sq. in.	Annealing Temperature °C.	Proportional Limit Annealed Lbs. per sq. in.
Commercial Palladium..................	31,800	800	4,500
3% Rhodium, 2% Ruthenium Palladium..	46,000	1000	16,000
1% Rhodium, 4% Ruthenium Palladium..	46,300	1100	21,000

WORKING TECHNOLOGY

Palladium is very ductile and can be worked hot or cold. As with platinum, it is usual to begin working ingots at about 800°C to secure more rapid reduction and then finish by cold working. Palladium withstands drastic cold working and, like gold, can be beaten into leaf as thin as 1/250,000 of an inch.

It is possible that pure palladium can be annealed at a lower temperature than pure platinum but reliable information is not available. Although marked softening occurs at 700°C, commercial palladium requires an annealing temperature of 800 or 900°C to obtain maximum ductility with a short anneal. At temperatures outside this range, selective grain growth resulting in lowered ductility may occur in some lots of commercial palladium.

Palladium is preferably annealed in nitrogen or carbon monoxide as it oxidizes in air if the temperature is below about 800°C, and it is hardened somewhat transiently, if allowed to cool in hydrogen. The oxide coating formed on palladium in air at temperatures above about 400°C has a narrow range of stability and decomposes at about 800°C. Hence, the discoloration caused by the oxide can be avoided by quenching in water from temperatures above about 800°C or by quenching in a reducing agent, such as water containing 5% alcohol or 5% formic acid. Alternatively, the oxide may be reduced cathodically in dilute sulphuric acid. Palladium can also be annealed in hydrogen without hardening if it is removed and cooled in air after annealing. However, marked hardening occurs if it is annealed and rapidly cooled in hydrogen. Thus, Wise and Eash (27) found that the tensile strength of palladium was raised from 30,000 lbs. per sq. in. to 48,000 lbs. per sq. in. and the elongation lowered from 38% in 2″ to 28% by cooling in hydrogen from 800°C. Alternate oxidizing and reducing annealing atmospheres are apt to produce blistering and surface damage and hence should be avoided.

CORROSION AND TARNISH RESISTANCE

Palladium is resistant to corrosion at room temperature by hydrofluoric acid, perchloric acid, phosphoric acid and acetic acid. It is slightly attacked by sulphuric, hydrochloric and hydrobromic acids, especially in the presence of air, and readily attacked by nitric acid, ferric chloride, hypochlorites and moist chlorine, bromine and iodine. In ordinary atmospheres palladium is resistant to tarnish, but some discoloration may occur on exposure to moist industrial atmospheres containing sulphur dioxide.

USES

Pure palladium is an excellent material for electrical contacts and large quantities are used in relays for telephone service. Dentistry employs a substantial amount of palladium as an alloying element in complex wrought and cast dental alloys. In these alloys, palladium improves the strength, toughness and the response to heat treatment in addition to substantially increasing the resistance to tarnish. It is also a most effective addition for raising the melting point of wrought dental wires, thereby permitting the use of higher grade, higher melting solders for the construction of restorations.

In finely divided form, usually applied to a suitable support, it is an exceptionally effective hydrogenation catalyst and finds application in special instances. Thin palladium septa for the selective diffusion or "filtering" of hydrogen are employed for special purifications of this gas.

Beaten into leaf, palladium is used for white non-tarnishing decorative effects in book binding, glass signs and trim. It can be electrodeposited from a number of baths, notably the complex nitrites and palladosamine chloride solutions, and has been used as a decorative plate. A recently developed high speed plating bath is also suitable for the production of heavy electrodeposits and for electroforming. Hardened with ruthenium and rhodium, palladium finds use as a jewelry alloy comparable to the jewelry golds. Palladium salts are employed in the production of special photographic printing papers where warm tones and permanence are desired. Solutions of palladous chloride also find use for detecting carbon monoxide in mines and other confined spaces.

The important uses of palladium in alloyed forms are given in the alloy sections which follow.

IRIDIUM

Iridium is the second member of the third series of transition elements and has an atomic weight of 193.1 and an atomic number of 77.

DENSITY Holborn and co-workers (54) determined the density of iridium as 22.41 gms/cm^3 at 20°C which is slightly lower than that observed for osmium. However, the density of iridium calculated from the space lattice, which with these particular elements may be more reliable, is 22.65$_6$ gms/cm^3 at 0°C and 22.65$_0$ at 20°C according to Owen and Yates (3). Hence available data do not warrant selection of either one of these metals as the densest metal known, although osmium traditionally has been credited with this property.

LATTICE Iridium has a face centered cubic lattice with a unit cell a_0 of 3.8312 ± .0005 A at 20°C according to Owen and Yates (3).

ALLOTROPY Neither the specific heat data nor the thermo electric force of a platinum-iridium couple give any indication of allotropic transformations.

THERMAL PROPERTIES

MELTING POINT From the brightness ratios of freezing gold and iridium Henning and Wensel (55) and Morris and Scholes (37) determined the melting point of iridium as 2454 ± 3°C.

BOILING POINT Richardson (38) estimated the boiling point as 5300°C by an arc method.

VAPOR PRESSURE From data on the differential volatilization and the estimated boiling points, it is believed that the vapor pressure of iridium is intermediate between that of osmium and ruthenium. However, iridium loses weight at a greater rate than platinum when heated in air as the oxide has a relatively high vapor pressure. According to Crookes (8), the loss of iridium in air at 1300°C is 10 times that of palladium, 30 times that of platinum and 60 times that of rhodium. Holborn and Austin (10) report that the loss of iridium on heating in air is 10 times that of platinum, while the loss in air at 25 mm is only one-eighth that in air at 760 mm, and the loss in oxygen is 11 times that in air at 760 mm.

THERMAL CONDUCTIVITY The thermal conductivity of iridium is 0.141 cal/sec. cm^2 °C/cm at 17°C and 0.135 at 100°C according to Barrat and Winter (56).

THERMAL EXPANSION The mean temperature coefficient of linear expansion between 0 and 100°C is 6.8 x 10^{-6} according to Holborn and Valentiner (57). They also report that the length for temperatures up to 1000°C can be calculated from the relation: $1_t = 1_0 (1 + 6.6967 \times 10^{-6}t + 1.158 \times 10^{-9} t^2)$.

Values calculated from this relation are given in Table 23.

TABLE 23
Thermal Expansion of Iridium

Temperature ° C.	Ratio Lt/Lo
0	1.00000
100	1.00068
200	1.00138
300	1.0021
400	1.0029
500	1.0036
600	1.0044
700	1.0052
800	1.0061
900	1.0070
1000	1.0078

SPECIFIC HEAT Jaeger and Rosenbohm (58) give 0.0307 cal/gm for the specific heat of iridium at 0°C. Between 0° and 1700°C the specific heat can be represented by the relation

$$c_p = 0.030725 + 7.4004 \times 10^{-6}t$$

In Table 24 values calculated from this relation are listed:

TABLE 24
Specific Heat of Iridium

Temperature ° C.	Specific Heat cal/gm
0	0.030725
100	0.0315
200	0.0322
300	0.0329
400	0.0337
500	0.0344
600	0.0352
700	0.0359
800	0.0366
900	0.0374
1000	0.0381
1100	0.0389
1200	0.0396
1300	0.0403
1400	0.0411
1500	0.0418
1600	0.0426
1700	0.0433

ELECTRICAL PROPERTIES

ELECTRICAL RESISTIVITY Jaeger and Diesselhorst's (11) value of 5.3 microhm-cm at 20°C is probably the best value for the electrical resistivity of iridium. Using this value and Holborn's (59) temperature coefficient, the values for the electrical resistivity at 0°, 100° and 500°C are calculated as 4.92, 6.85, and 15.1 microhm-cm respectively.

TEMPERATURE COEFFICIENT OF ELECTRICAL RESISTANCE Holborn (59) reported 0.003925 per °C for the temperature coefficient of electrical resistance of iridium over the range 0-100°C. This value increases with increasing temperature as shown in Table 25.

TABLE 25
Temperature Coefficient of Electrical Resistivity of Iridium

Temperature Range ° C.	Temperature Coefficient per ° C.
0–100	.003925
0–200	.00398
0–300	.00404
0–400	.00408
0–500	.00414

THERMAL ELECTROMOTIVE FORCE AGAINST PLATINUM Holborn and Day (60) measured the thermal electromotive force of platinum-iridium couple at temperatures up to 1500°C. Their values are shown in Table 26.

MAGNETIC SUSCEPTIBILITY M. Owen (61) gave 0.129×10^{-6} mass units for the magnetic susceptibility of iridium at room temperature while Honda (47) gave a higher value of 0.15×10^{-6} mass units. Values for the magnetic suscep-

TABLE 26
Thermal EMF Developed by a Iridium-Platinum Couple

Temperature °C.	EMF Millivolts
0	0
100	+0.65
300	2.47
500	4.78
700	7.56
900	10.80
1100	14.48
1300	18.47
1500	22.50

tibility at higher temperatures are given on page 24.

COLOR AND REFLECTIVITY

The color of iridium is similar to that of platinum although it has a slight yellow cast. According to von Wartenberg (48) the specular reflectivity of iridium is 75% at 0.579 μ. Auwarter (188) gives 64%, 70%, 75% and 78% at 0.45, 0.55, 0.65 and 0.75 μ, respectively. Coblentz (22) gives 78% at 1.0 μ and Kenworthy (49) reports 70% for the mean specular reflectivity with a somewhat reddish light.

MECHANICAL PROPERTIES

Because of the difficulty of working iridium, few of its mechanical properties have been determined.

The Brinell hardness of cast iridium has been reported as 163 BHN by Nemilow (62), 172 BHN by Rydberg (63), and 217 BHN by Edwards (64). Atkinson (65) gave 255 VHN for the Vickers hardness of hot forged iridium.

WORKING TECHNOLOGY

Iridium is even more difficult to work than rhodium, but it may be hot forged at high temperatures (1200-1500°C). It is probable that the presence of traces of non-metallic impurities in commercial iridium contribute to the difficulty encountered in working it.

CORROSION RESISTANCE

Iridium is the most corrosion resistant element known; it is unaffected by common acids and is even resistant to aqua regia and fuming sulphuric acid. Small percentages of iridium, up to about 20% also greatly increase the corrosion resistance of platinum and palladium.

USES

The main use of iridium is as a hardening addition to platinum. Iridium hardened platinum alloys are preferred for jewelry in the United States; they are also employed for electrical contacts and for chemical and electrochemical equipment which is not subject to especially high temperatures. Small amounts of iridium, up to about 0.1%, are used for refining the grain size and improving the mechanical properties of gold and silver base casting alloys.

Pure iridium has been used for crucibles in studying slag equilibria at very high temperatures. It has also been electrodeposited but so far no commercial use has been made of iridium in this form.

RHODIUM

Rhodium is the second member of the second series of transition elements and has an atomic number of 45 and an atomic weight of 102.91.

DENSITY Recent determinations of the density average 12.4 gms/cm^3 at 20 °C. This value is in agreement with those calculated from the lattice constants which are 12.42 at 0°C and 12.414 at 20°C according to Owen and Yates (3).

LATTICE Rhodium has a face centered cubic lattice with a unit cell a_0 of 3.7957 ± .0003 A at 20°C (3).

ALLOTROPY Jaeger and Zanstra (34) attributed new lines in the X-ray spectrogram of finely divided rhodium, obtained by the reduction of salts or by electrolysis, to an alpha modification of rhodium which is the most stable form at lower temperatures and occurs in addition to the beta form of wrought rhodium. The alpha modification has a simple cubic lattice with a unit cell of 9.211 A and appears to be stable up to 1000°C but diminishes in quantity as the temperature increases. The specific heat-temperature curve has a maximum in the neighborhood of 1200°C according to Jaeger and Rosenbohm (66) and this tends to support the above conclusions. However, there is no evidence of allotropic transformations in the thermal electromotive force-temperature curve of a pure platinum-pure rhodium couple.

THERMAL PROPERTIES

MELTING POINT Measuring the brightness ratios of freezing gold and rhodium, Roeser and Wensel (67) determined the melting point of rhodium as 1966 ± 3°C. Later Barber and Schofield (197) redetermined the melting point by the same method and obtained the same value.

BOILING POINT Using an arc method, Richardson (38) estimated 4500°C for the boiling point of rhodium.

VAPOR PRESSURE From the estimated boiling points, it is believed that the vapor pressure of rhodium is about the same as that of platinum. Holborn and Austin (10) report that the loss on heating in air is the same as that of platinum. They also report that the loss in oxygen is five times as great as that in air at atmospheric pressure, while in air at 25 mm, the loss is about one-half that in air at 760 mm. The weight loss of rhodium in nitrogen is very small. Crookes (8) reports that the loss at 1300 °C in air is only one-half that of platinum, one-sixth that of palladium and one-sixtieth that of iridium. Thus, as in the case of platinum, the loss on heating in air is associated with the formation of a volatile oxide. According to Wohler and Muller (68), the oxide begins to form at about 600°C and dissociates at 1115°C.

THERMAL CONDUCTIVITY The thermal conductivity of rhodium is 0.213 cal/sec cm^2 °C/cm at 0°C, 0.210 at 17°C and 0.192 at 100°C according to Barrat and Winter (56).

THERMAL EXPANSION Ebert (69) gave 8.5 x 10^{-6} for the mean coefficient of thermal expansion between 0 and 100°C. Over the range 20 to 100°C Swanger (70) gave 8.3 x 10^{-6} and Holzmann (40) 7.8 x 10^{-6}. Ebert measured the change in length of a rhodium specimen 1 meter long at 0°C and obtained values shown in Table 27. According to Holzmann, the length for temperatures up to 1000°C can be calculated from the relation $l_t = l_{20}\,[1 + 7.628 \times 10^{-6}\,(t-20) + 2.268 \times 10^{-9}\,(t-20)^2]$ where l_{20} is the length at 20°C and t is the temperature.

TABLE 27
Thermal Expansion of Rhodium

Temperature ° C.	Lt/Lo
0	1.00000
50	1.00040
100	1.00085
200	1.00180
300	1.00280
400	1.00385
500	1.00490
600	1.00600
700	1.00710
800	1.00825
900	1.00950
1000	1.01080
1100	1.0121
1200	1.0135
1300	1.0150
1400	1.0165
1500	1.0181

SPECIFIC HEAT Holzmann's (40) values for the specific heat of rhodium at 0°, 100° and 1000° are 0.0604, 0.0623 and 0.0788 cal/gram respectively while Jaeger and Rosenbohm (66) give 0.0589 at 0°C, 0.0603 at 100°C and 0.0797 at 1000°C. Jaeger and Rosenbohm give the relation $c_p = 0.05893 + 1.066 \times 10^{-5}t + 2.7744 \times 10^{-8}t^2 - 1.7642 \times 10^{-11}t^3$ for the specific heat at temperatures up to 1300°C. This relation indicates a maximum in the neighborhood of 1200°C. According to Holzmann, the specific heat of rhodium for temperatures up to 1000°C is given by the relation: $c_p = 0.060467 + 1.8303 \times 10^{-5}t$.

Values calculated from these equations are given in Table 28.

TABLE 28
Specific Heat of Rhodium

Temperature ° C.	Specific Heat cal/gram	
	Jaeger and Rosenbohm	Holzmann
0	0.05893	0.060467
100	0.0602	0.0623
200	0.0620	0.0641
300	0.0641	0.0659
400	0.0665	0.0678
500	0.0690	0.0696
600	0.0715	0.0714
700	0.0739	0.0733
800	0.0762	0.0751
900	0.0781	0.0769
1000	0.0797	0.0788
1100	0.0807	......
1200	0.0812	......
1300	0.0809	......

ELECTRICAL PROPERTIES

ELECTRICAL RESISTIVITY The latest determination of the electrical resistivity of rhodium is that of Roeser and Wensel (67) who obtained the value 4.3 microhm-cm at 0°C. This sample evidently was quite pure, since it had a higher temperature coefficient of electrical resistance than had previously been reported by others for rhodium. The resistivities at 20° and 100°C as calculated from these data are 4.6$_8$ and 6.2$_6$ microhm-cm respectively. Earlier measurements of 4.93 microhm-cm at 20°C and 4.58 microhm-cm at 0°C had been reported by Swanger (70) and Gruneisen (71).

TEMPERATURE COEFFICIENT OF ELECTRICAL RESISTANCE Roeser and Wensel's (67) value for the temperature coefficient of electrical resistance $\left(\frac{R_{100} - R_0}{100\ R_0}\right)$ of rhodium is 0.00457. Holborn (59) gave 0.004428, Acken (72) 0.0044, Swanger (70) and Brenner (73) 0.00436. Holborn's values for the ratio R_t/R_0 for higher temperatures are given in Table 29.

TABLE 29
Relative Electrical Resistivity of Rhodium

Temperature ° C.	Ratio R_t/R_0
0	1.0000
100	1.4428
199.1	1.8985
309.25	2.4273
406.1	2.9184
408.1	2.9293
509.3	3.4637
510.7	3.4710

THERMOELECTRIC FORCE AGAINST PLATINUM Three of the four investigators determining the thermoelectric force produced by a platinum-rhodium couple obtained results which agree very well and the other values are in fair agreement. Caldwell's (19) values, which are the latest, are listed in Table 30.

MAGNETIC SUSCEPTIBILITY M. Owen (61) gave 1.08 x 10^{-6} mass units for the magnetic susceptibility. Honda's (209, 210) values for the magnetic susceptibility of rhodium at temperatures up to 1100°C are given on page 24.

TABLE 30
Thermal EMF of Rhodium vs. Platinum

Temperature ° C.	EMF Millivolts
0	0
100	+ 0.70
200	+ 1.61
300	+ 2.68
400	+ 3.91
500	+ 5.28
600	+ 6.77
700	+ 8.40
800	+10.16
900	+12.04
1000	+14.05
1100	+16.18
1200	+18.42

COLOR AND REFLECTIVITY

Rhodium is similar to platinum in color but has a slight reddish cast and a considerably higher reflectivity. In the visible spectrum the specular reflectivity is close to 80%. Coblentz and Stair's (75) and Heraeus's (76) values for the specular reflectivity are given in Table 31. Auwarter (188, 198) gives similar values for the reflectivity of rhodium. He also gives data on the optical characteristics of rhodium surfaced glass with reflecting or partly transparant rhodium coatings.

TABLE 31
Specular Reflectivity of Rhodium

Wave Length m μ	Specular Reflectivity Per Cent	
	Coblentz and Stair	Heraeus
250	48	. .
300	57	72
400	69	78
500	73	79
600	78	80
700	79	82
800	81	84
900	. .	85
1000	84	86
1200	. .	88
1400	88	89
1600	89	90.5
1800	. .	92
2000	91	93
2500	91	94
3000	. .	95

Because of the high reflectivity of rhodium and its high resistance to tarnish at ordinary and moderately elevated temperatures rhodium electroplates are used for surfacing searchlight, headlight and motion picture reflectors as well as for finishing silverware and jewelry.

Values for the emissivity of rhodium are given on page 24.

MECHANICAL PROPERTIES

Values ranging from 55 BHN (Nemilow and Voronow) (77) to 156 BHN (Edwards) (64) have been reported for the hardness of annealed rhodium. Acken (72) reported a Brinell hardness of 101 and a Vickers hardness of 122 for rhodium annealed at 1200°C and these values are probably the best of those so far determined. Carter (17) gave 260 BHN for the hardness of cold rolled rhodium and 139 BHN for the hardness of cast rhodium.

According to Atkinson and Raper (78), the hardness of rhodium electroplate deposited from the sulphate bath is 549-641 VHN. This determination was made by the National Physical Laboratories using a machine similar to the Vickers but employing small loads of the order of 20 grams.

WORKING TECHNOLOGY

According to Swanger (70) and Sivil (31), cast high purity rhodium is not workable cold, but can be readily forged at temperatures above 800°C. The hot worked metal is coarse grained and is not ductile at room temperature, but by continuing to work the metal at gradually decreasing temperatures a fibrous structure is developed and the metal becomes ductile and moderately workable at room temperature. Wrought rhodium may be adequately softened by annealing at 800°C and in this condition may be cold worked about 40%. Rhodium is superficially oxidized in air at temperatures above about 600°C (the oxide dissociates at about 1100°C in air) and hence is preferably annealed in an inert atmosphere.

CORROSION RESISTANCE

The corrosion resistance of rhodium is exceptionally high and is almost equal to that of iridium. It resists corrosion by most common acids and other corrosive chemicals, including aqua regia, but is slightly attacked by hydrobromic acid containing free bromine and by hypochlorites. It is also readily attacked by fuming sulphuric acid at 300°C. Like iridium, rhodium additions generally improve the corrosion resistance of platinum and palladium, while the rhodium nickel alloys containing 37% rhodium are more resistant to corrosion than 14 Kt. gold.

USES

Rhodium is used mainly as an alloying addition to platinum and palladium or as an electroplate. It moderately hardens platinum, increases the solidus temperature, and decreases grain growth at elevated temperatures. Generally, the 10% rhodium platinum alloy is used for furnace windings, thermocouple elements, linings for nozzles for extruding glass, bushings for glass fiber production, rayon spinnerets, electrodes for aircraft spark plugs and as the catalyst for the oxidation of ammonia in the production of nitric acid. The 5% rhodium platinum alloy is also being employed for the latter purpose. The 3½% rhodium platinum alloy is extensively used for crucibles in the United States.

Rhodium, in conjunction with ruthenium, is added to jewelry grade palladium to harden it and increase its resistance to the nitric acid drop test which is commonly used to determine the carat of jewelry gold. Rhodium is also a component in many of the high grade hard pen tipping alloys. Rhodium provides a non-tarnishing electroplate with high reflectivity and in this form finds extensive use as a finishing plate in the jewelry field and for reflectors for motion picture projectors, aircraft searchlights and the like. Mirrors or reflectors with high reflectivity and chemical stability are also made by depositing rhodium on glass by distillation in vacuo. Thin coatings on glass provide perfect gray filters.

OSMIUM

Osmium is the first member of the third series of transition elements and has an atomic number of 76 and an atomic weight of 190.2.

DENSITY Joly and Vezes (79) reported the density as 22.48 gm/cm^3. Owen and co-workers (80) calculated the density from the space lattice as 22.61 gms/cm^3 at 18°C, while direct determinations gave 22.41 gms/cm^3 at this temperature. Either osmium or iridium is the densest element known, but present data do not permit selection between the two.

LATTICE Osmium has a hexagonal close packed lattice with an a_0 of 2.7304 ± 0.0005 A and an axial ratio c/a of 1.5785 at 18°C according to Owen and co-workers (80).

ALLOTROPY Since the specific heat-temperature relation is linear and other properties give no indication of transformations, it is assumed that osmium is devoid of allotropic transformations.

THERMAL PROPERTIES

MELTING POINT The melting point of osmium has not been determined but it is believed to be about 2700°C.

BOILING POINT Using an arc method, Richardson (38) estimated the boiling point of osmium to be about 5500°C, which is highest of the platinum group metals.

VAPOR PRESSURE When heated in air, osmium loses weight rapidly due to the oxidation of the metal and subsequent volatilization of the low boiling point oxide. Osmium itself, however, has the lowest vapor pressure of the platinum group metals. This and the high melting point led to the use of osmium filament incandescent lamps for a short time prior to the advent of tungsten filament lamps.

THERMAL EXPANSION Fizeau (81) reported the temperature coefficient of linear expansion as 6.57 x 10^{-6} per °C at 40°C.

SPECIFIC HEAT According to Jaeger and Rosenbohm (66) the specific heat of osmium is 0.0309 cal/gm at 0°C. For temperatures between 0 and 1600°C, the specific heat can be represented by the rela-

TABLE 32
Specific Heat of Osmium

Temperature ° C.	Specific Heat cal/gm
0	0.030986
100	0.0314
200	0.0319
300	0.0324
400	0.0329
500	0.0333
600	0.0338
700	0.0343
800	0.0348
900	0.0352
1000	0.0357
1100	0.0362
1200	0.0366
1300	0.0371
1400	0.0376
1500	0.0381
1600	0.0385

tion $c_p = 0.030986 + 4.721 \times 10^{-6}$ t. Values calculated from this relation are given in Table 32.

ELECTRICAL PROPERTIES

ELECTRICAL RESISTIVITY The specific electrical resistivity of osmium is 9.5 microhm-cm at 20°C according to Blau (82).

TEMPERATURE COEFFICIENT OF ELECTRICAL RESISTANCE Lombardi (83) gave .0042 per °C as the temperature coefficient of electrical resistance over the range 0-100°C.

MAGNETIC SUSCEPTIBILITY The magnetic susceptibility of osmium is 0.048×10^{-6} mass units at room temperature according to Owen (61). Honda and Sone (84) gave 0.074×10^{-6} mass units.

MECHANICAL PROPERTIES

The mechanical properties of osmium have not been investigated. Quite pure cast osmium has a Vickers hardness of about 350 VHN.

WORKING TECHNOLOGY

Because of its hexagonal structure and high melting point, osmium would be expected to be difficult to work. It is brittle even at very high temperatures and as yet has not been worked. The oxide is very poisonous and is especially irritating to the eyes, lungs and other mucous membranes which readily reduce it. Melting operations must, therefore, be conducted in a fume hood.

CORROSION RESISTANCE

Osmium is believed to be somewhat less resistant to corrosion than some of the other platinum metals, but reliable data are not available due to the difficulty of obtaining satisfactory samples of the metal for tests.

USES

The principal uses of osmium are in hard, pen-tipping and phonograph needle alloys and special hard electrical contact alloys some of which contain tungsten carbide. Osmic acid is suitable for the detection of finger prints and for staining fatty tissue for microscopic examination.

RUTHENIUM

Ruthenium is the first element in the second series of transition elements. It has an atomic weight of 101.7 and an atomic number of 44.

DENSITY The value of 12.2 gms/cm^3 was selected as the most representative value for the density of ruthenium at 20°C although reliable data are not available. Owen and co-workers (80) calculated the density from the space lattice as 12.45 gms/cm^3 at 18°C.

LATTICE Ruthenium, like osmium, has a hexagonal close packed lattice with a unit cell a_0 of 2.6987 ± 0.0005 A and an axial ratio of 1.5833 at 18°C (80).

ALLOTROPY According to Jaeger and Rosenbohm (58) the specific heat data indicate the existence of four allotropic forms with transition points at 1035°, 1200° and 1500°C. However, these investigators also studied the thermal electromotive force of a platinum-ruthenium couple which gave no evidence of allotropy so that the question remains open.

THERMAL PROPERTIES

MELTING POINT The melting point of ruthenium has not been accurately determined but it is known to be above 2400°C and perhaps above 2450°C.

BOILING POINT Richardson (38) estimated the boiling point as 4900°C.

VAPOR PRESSURE Although the vapor pressure of ruthenium has not been determined, it is believed to be of the same order as that of platinum. The oxide, however, is quite volatile and this accounts for the relatively high losses observed on heating ruthenium in air. According to Crooks (8), the loss of weight of ruthenium in air at 1300°C is about 7 times that of iridium, 350 times that of platinum and 700 times that of rhodium.

THERMAL EXPANSION Fizeau (81) gave 9.1 x 10^{-6} for the coefficient of linear expansion at 20°C and 9.6 x 10^{-6} at 40°C.

SPECIFIC HEAT The specific heat of ruthenium has been studied by Holzmann (40) and Jaeger and Rosenbohm (58). The latter investigators conclude that there are four allotropic forms of ruthenium with transition points at 1035°, 1200°, and 1500°C. They report that the specific heat of the alpha form between 0 and 1000°C can be represented by the relation $c_p = 0.055066 + 1.61676 \times 10^{-5}\, t$ while Holzmann gives $c_p = 0.057439 + 1.8921 \times 10^{-5}\, t$ for the same range. Jaeger and Rosenbohm give the following relations for the specific heats at temperatures above 1000°C;

between 1000 and 1070°C.

$$c_p = 0.070641 + 5.7905 \times 10^{-4} (t-1000) - 7.5736 \times 10^{-6} (t-1000)^2$$

between 1070 and 1200°C.

$$c_p = 0.062078 + 4.0379 \times 10^{-6}\, t$$

between 1200 and 1400°C.

$c_p = 0.055949 + 1.4238 \times 10^{-5} t$

and between 1400 and 1600°C.

$c_p = 0.074615 + 5.4752 \times 10^{-4} (t-1400) - 3.187 \times 10^{-6} (t-1400)^2$.

Values for the specific heats at high temperatures are given in Table 33. However, further work is required to definitely establish the existence of the four allotropic forms.

TABLE 33
Specific Heat of Ruthenium

Temperature ° C.	Specific Heat cal/gm	
	Holzmann	Jaeger and Rosenbohm
0	0.057439	0.055066
100	0.0593	0.0567
200	0.0612	0.0583
300	0.0631	0.0599
400	0.0650	0.0615
500	0.0669	0.0631
600	0.0688	0.0648
700	0.0707	0.0664
800	0.0726	0.0680
900	0.0745	0.0696
1000	0.0764	0.0712
1070	......	0.0664
1100	......	0.0665
1200	......	0.0730
1300	......	0.0745
1400	......	0.0745
1450	......	0.0940
1500	......	0.1075
1550	......	0.0850
1600	......	0.0566

ELECTRICAL PROPERTIES

ELECTRICAL RESISTIVITY Benedicks (85) gave 14.4 microhms-cm for the electrical resistivity of ruthenium at 18°C.

THERMOELECTRIC FORCE AGAINST PLATINUM Jaeger and Rosenbohm (58) determined the thermoelectric force produced by a platinum-ruthenium couple and obtained values shown in Table 34.

TABLE 34
Thermal EMF of a Ruthenium-Platinum Couple

Temperature ° C.	EMF Millivolts
0	0
400	3.867
600	6.737
800	10.097
1000	13.951
1200	18.317
1400	22.991
1600	27.978

MAGNETIC SUSCEPTIBILITY M. Owen (61) gave 0.895×10^{-6} mass units for the magnetic susceptibility of ruthenium. Honda's values for the magnetic susceptibility at higher temperatures are given on page 24.

COLOR AND REFLECTIVITY

The color of ruthenium is similar to that of platinum. Kenworthy (49) gave 63% for the mean specular reflectivity with a somewhat reddish light.

MECHANICAL PROPERTIES

The Brinell hardness of cast ruthenium is 220 BHN according to Carter (17). Atkinson (65) reports 390 VHN for the Vickers hardness of hot forged ruthenium.

WORKING TECHNOLOGY

Ruthenium, in common with most metals with a hexagonal structure, is difficult to work and its high melting point and the volatility and unpleasant odor of its oxide further aggravate the working troubles. However, with care and persistence, the pure metal can be forged at temperatures of about 1500°C but even at this temperature it is hard, not readily reduced by hammering and subject to edge cracking. The loss due to the volatilization of the oxide may be minimized by playing a hydrogen flame over the metal. Melting and working are best done in a fume hood with a good draught in order to keep the unpleasant fumes away from the operator. These precautions are not necessary for the workable platinum ruthenium and palladium ruthenium alloys which can be melted in air without appreciable loss of ruthenium and, considering their high hardness, worked without undue difficulty. For example, the 10 to 15% ruthenium platinum alloys are relatively easy to hot work and can be moderately cold worked after preliminary hot work. The 5% ruthenium platinum alloy, which has properties similar to the 10% iridium platinum alloy, can be readily cold worked without preliminary hot working.

CORROSION RESISTANCE

The general corrosion resistance of ruthenium approaches that of iridium. It is unaffected by common acids at room temperature or 100°C. It is also unaffected by fuming sulphuric acid at 300°C or by aqua regia. Like iridium and rhodium, ruthenium additions generally improve the corrosion resistance of platinum and palladium.

USES

Rarely employed in the elemental form, ruthenium is mainly used as a hardener for platinum or palladium. It is a very effective hardener for platinum, the 5% ruthenium platinum alloy having properties similar to the 10% iridium platinum alloy, and ruthenium hardened platinum is becoming increasingly popular as an alternative to iridium platinum. Ruthenium, usually in conjunction with rhodium, is used as a hardener for jewelry grade palladium. It is also employed in certain hard alloys used for tipping the nibs of fountain pens and for phonograph needles. Minor additions, of the order of 0.1%, of ruthenium are used to refine the grain size and improve the mechanical properties of gold and silver base casting alloys, particularly those used in dentistry.

Ruthenium catalysts are sometimes employed in hydrogenations and they appear to be the best catalysts for the synthesis of hydrocarbons of very high molecular weights. What appear to be rather hard electrodeposits have been secured from complex nitrite, nitroso and other baths, but thus far no use has been made of them.

PLATINUM ALLOYS

ANTIMONY PLATINUM

Friederich and Leroux (127) and Nemilow and Voronow (128) investigated this system and obtained slightly different results. However, it is evident that an eutectic between the compound $PtSb_2$ (56% antimony) and platinum occurs at about 24% antimony and about 670°C. At least two compounds are formed by peritectic reactions, Pt_4Sb (13% antimony) at about 700°C and PtSb (38% antimony) at about 1050°C. Friederich and Leroux found evidence of another compound, Pt_5Sb_2, at 630°C but this was not confirmed by Nemilow and Voronow who attributed the thermal arrest at this temperature to the eutectic transformation. The compound $PtSb_2$ (56% antimony) melts at about 1220°C. There is probably a solid solution range at the platinum end of the series, but the solid solubility of antimony in platinum is believed to be small.

ARSENIC PLATINUM

According to Friederich and Leroux (129), an eutectic between the compound Pt_2As_3 (37% arsenic) and platinum occurs at about 13% arsenic and 597°C. Several compounds are believed to be formed at high arsenic contents. The solid solubility of arsenic in platinum has not been determined but is believed to be very small. Fischer (180) found that traces of arsenic in platinum crucibles result in embrittlement due to the formation of the brittle fusible eutectic. Early workers used arsenic to render platinum fusible. Castings made from this alloy were heated to volatilize the arsenic and then hammered to close the pores, but the resulting product was not very satisfactory.

BORON PLATINUM

This system has not been investigated but from the work of Pearson (211) it is evident that a low melting eutectic is formed, probably between platinum and a platinum boride.

A novel resistor of high negative temperature coefficient of resistance, made by joining a platinum wire to a boron crystal, is the only known use of these alloys. The resistance depends largely upon the area of the platinum boride interface.

CALCIUM PLATINUM

Although this system has not been investigated in detail, the fact that platinum melted in lime crucibles under reducing conditions is difficult to work, indicates that even small amounts of calcium form an insoluble low melting or brittle compound with platinum. Age hardening of low calcium content platinum alloys, observed by Sivil (26), confirms the suspected low solid solubility of calcium.

Small amounts, of the order of 0.01%, of calcium increase the tensile strength and markedly raise the annealing temperature of platinum according to Carter (51) and Sivil (26). As previously noted the low calcium content alloys may be age hardened.

CARBON PLATINUM

It is known that molten platinum readily takes up carbon and rejects it as graphite on solidifying and it appears from the work of Collier, Harrison and Taylor (132) that carbon forms an eutectic with platinum which melts slightly below the melting point of platinum. The solid solubility of carbon in platinum has not been determined, but is believed to be less than 0.25% carbon at the solidus and doubtless decreases to minute values at low temperatures. Platinum containing rejected graphite is brittle.

CHROMIUM PLATINUM

The platinum chromium alloys have been studied by Gebhardt and Koster (215), Nemilow (123), Friederich and Kussmann (122) and Muller (120) but the data obtained are still insufficient to establish the exact nature of the system. Thermal analysis of the platinum-rich alloys, by Gebhardt and Koster, indicate that the liquidus and solidus are close together and fall smoothly, with increasing chromium, from the melting point of platinum to about 1400°C at about 50% chromium, where a eutectic or peritectic is formed. According to these investigators, the face centered cubic solid solution which forms on freezing extends to about 50% chromium at the solidus and can be retained by quenching from high temperatures. In platinum-rich alloys containing more than about 6% chromium, one or more transformations, which involve ordering, occur below about 1150°C. The composition of the compounds which appear to be involved, and their ranges of stability, have not been determined. On the basis of a hardness study, Nemilow concluded that $PtCr_2$ and PtCr are formed, but X-ray, microscopic and other studies indicate the probable existence of $PtCr_3$, PtCr and Pt_3Cr.

Alloys containing from about 6 to 17.5% chromium become ferromagnetic when heat treated or slowly cooled to develop the ordered face centered cubic lattice. Gebhardt and Koster found that the Curie temperature of these ordered alloys increases smoothly from about 100°C at 7.5% chromium to about 850°C at 17.5% chromium.

The chromium-rich alloys have not received much study but according to Friederich and Kussmann, a body centered cubic and a face centered cubic phase coexist in alloys containing more than about 50% chromium.

ELECTRICAL PROPERTIES

Carter (51) obtained 30.4 microhm-cm at 20°C for the electrical resistivity of the 2% chromium alloy while Nemilow (123) reported 65 microhm-cm at 25°C for the 3.8% chromium alloy.

MECHANICAL PROPERTIES

Hardness peaks occur at 15, 24.5 and 44.5% chromium according to Nemilow (123); the maximum hardness being 300 BHN at 15% chromium. According to Carter (51) the tensile strength of the annealed 2% chromium alloy is 44,000 lbs. per sq. in.

USES

Platinum-rich alloys may be useful for spark plug electrodes and certain types of heating resistors subject to contamination in use. They may also be suitable for catalysts.

COBALT PLATINUM

The platinum cobalt system has a rather flat minimum in the liquidus temperature curve at about 1450°C and 50% cobalt according to Nemilow (111) and Gebhardt and Koster (216). It is believed that the solidus lies close to the liquidus throughout and that a continuous series of solid solutions form on freezing. At lower temperatures, several reactions occur; the formation of a phase based upon PtCo, which at still lower temperatures undergoes ordering, and the allotropic changes of the cobalt-rich alloys. The phase based upon PtCo forms below 825°C at 23% cobalt, and extends from about 10 to 30% cobalt at room temperature according to Gebhardt and Koster. In this range, the face centered cubic lattice of the solid solution, transforms to an unordered face centered tetragonal lattice characteristic of the compound PtCo. At lower temperatures, beginning at about 510°C at 23% cobalt, this tetragonal lattice develops an ordered structure. In alloys containing more than about 70% cobalt, the allotropic transformation of cobalt is evident as shown in Figure 12. The Curie temperature of the 5% cobalt alloy is 50°C, according to Constant (112) and, for the solid solution alloys, it ascends smoothly with increasing cobalt to about 1115°C for pure cobalt, according to Gebhardt and Koster (216).

ELECTRICAL PROPERTIES

According to Gebhardt and Koster, the addition of cobalt to platinum results in a rapid increase in electrical resistivity to a maximum of about 45 microhm-cm in the range 10 to 20% cobalt after which the resistivity falls gradually with further increase in cobalt content as shown in Figure 13. The transformed alloys in the range 10 to 30% cobalt have lower resistivities, a minimum of about 27 microhm-cm being observed for the slowly cooled 23% cobalt alloy. Nemilow's (111) values for the electrical resistivity of the platinum-rich alloys are in agreement with those given by Gebhardt and Koster. Nemilow reports the temperature coefficient of electrical resistance of the 7% cobalt alloy as 0.00145 per °C over the range 25-100°C.

MECHANICAL PROPERTIES

Both Nemilow and Gebhardt and Koster determined the hardness of platinum cobalt alloys after slow cooling and Nemilow determined the hardness over most of the system after quenching. Based mainly on these data, it is believed that in the quenched condition the platinum cobalt system has a hardness peak of about 190 BHN at about 23% cobalt as shown in Figure 14. Nemilow's and Gebhardt and Koster's values for the hardness of

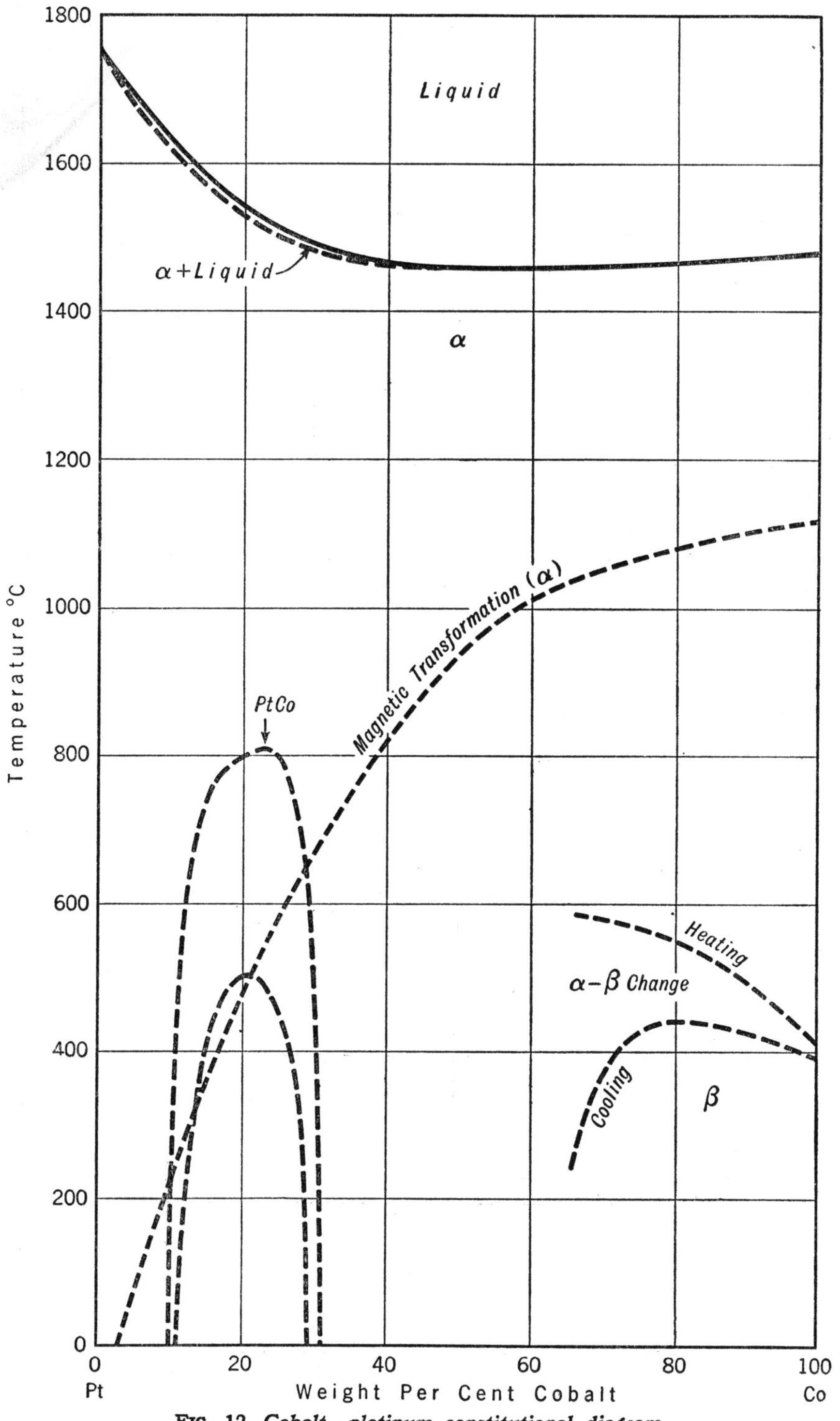

FIG. 12. *Cobalt—platinum constitutional diagram.*

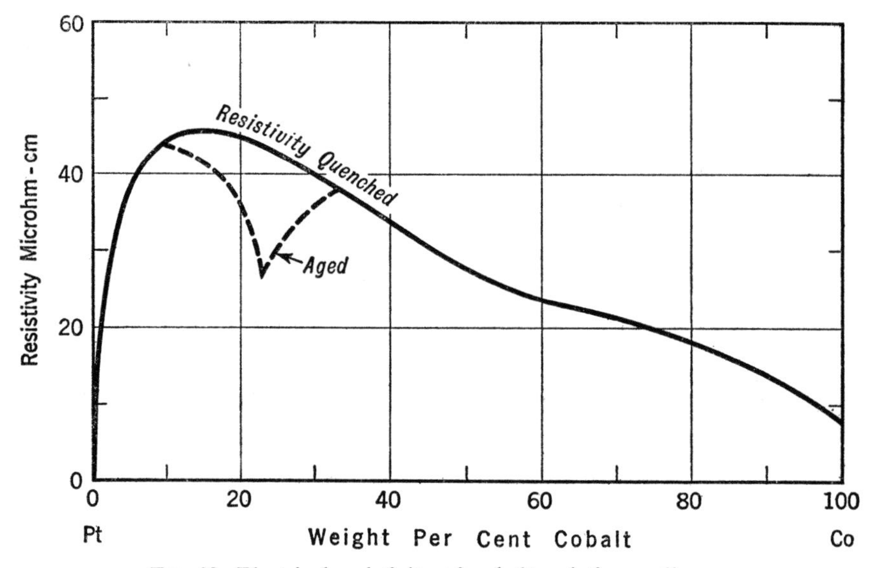

FIG. 13. *Electrical resistivity of cobalt—platinum alloys.*

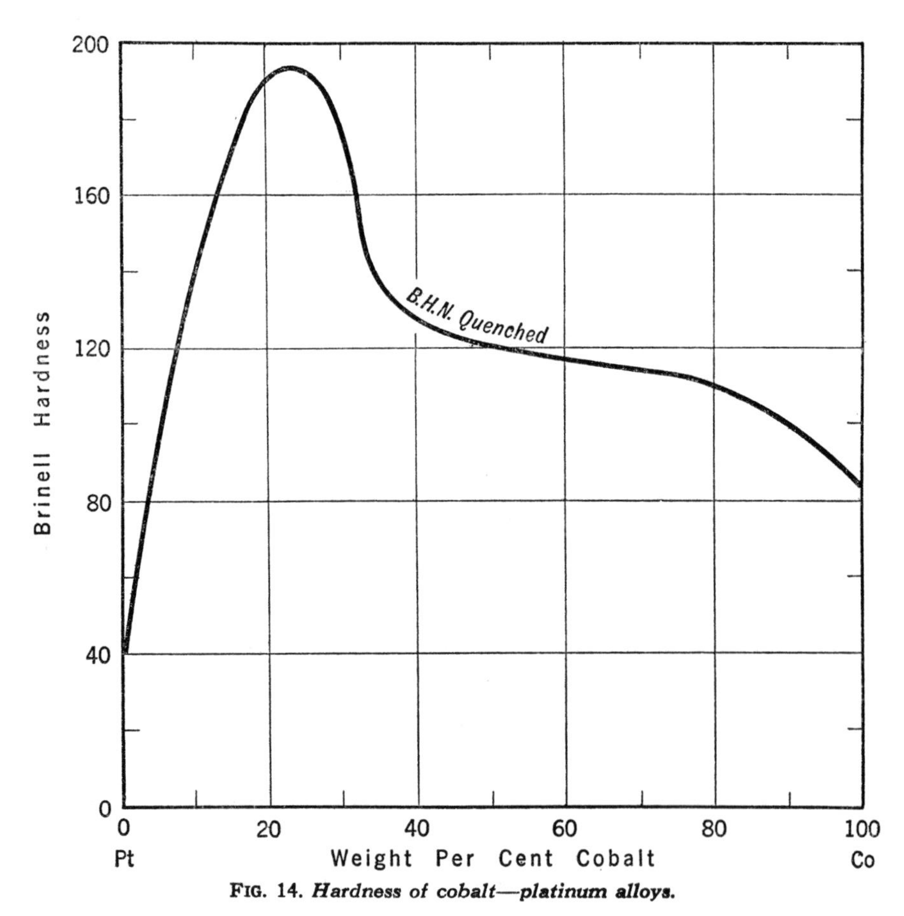

FIG. 14. *Hardness of cobalt—platinum alloys.*

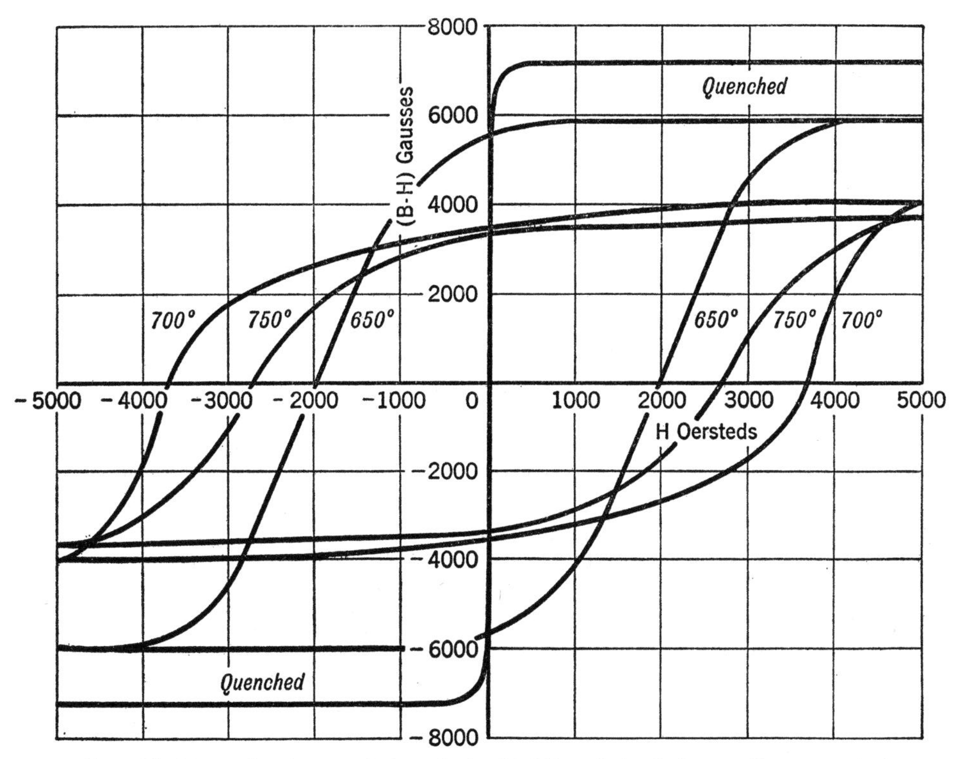

Fig. 15. *Magnetic characteristics of the 23.3% cobalt-platinum alloy quenched from 1000°C and aged for 30 minutes at indicated temperatures.*

slowly cooled alloys do not agree completely but show the same general trend and indicate that alloys within the range 70 to 90% cobalt are hardened by slow cooling. This hardening is probably a reflection of the allotropic transformation of cobalt which is evident within this compositional range. From Gebhardt and Koster's work, it is evident that quenched alloys in the neighborhood of 23% cobalt may also be hardened to a maximum of about 250 BHN by heat treatment at about 650°C for one half hour. Presumably the 23% cobalt alloy "over-ages" readily since hardnesses of this order were not obtained on slow cooling.

MAGNETIC PROPERTIES

Jellinghouse (113), Gebhardt and Koster (216), and Neumann (218) studied the alloys in the neighborhood of 23.3% (50 atomic percent) cobalt and found them to have extraordinary magnetic properties. For the 23.3% cobalt alloy, the coercive force, $_{\mathrm{I}}H_c$, is near 0.5 oersted when quenched from 1000°C, increases to 2000 oersteds when reheated at 650°C for one half hour and is at a maximum of about 3700 oersteds when reheated at 700°C for one half hour according to Gebhardt and Koster. The latter value would correspond to, $_{b}H_c$, of about 2500 oersteds. Figure 15 shows the effect of reheating temperature on the magnetic characteristics of this alloy when quenched from 1000°C. These investigators found that the quenched alloy is magnetically soft and that the product (B_r H_c) attains its maximum value when the quenched alloy is reheated at 700°C for one half hour.

Values given by Jellinghouse and Neumann are in agreement with those reported by Gebhardt and Koster for the aged alloys, but there is some doubt as to the heat treatment used by the former investigators. For the 23.3% cobalt alloy, Neumann (Figure 27) gives 2650 oersteds for the coercive force, ${}_bH_c$, 4530 gausses for the residual induction and 3,770,000 for the energy product $(BH)_{max.}$.

Recent work by D. L. Martin and A. H. Geisler (219) yielded much higher properties in the 48 atomic percent alloy—namely B_r 6,300 gausses and H_c 4,100 oersteds with an energy product $(BH)_{max.}$ of 9 x 10^6. This was the result of cooling from 1000°C to 200°C in 10 minutes followed by aging at 600°C for 5 hours.

The energy product of 9×10^6 is far higher than is obtainable from any other permanent magnet alloy.

USES

The extraordinary magnetic properties of the 23% cobalt alloy may lead to its use in small instrument magnets, particularly where a very short magnet is essential. Alloys containing a few percent of cobalt plus rhodium have been proposed for ammonia oxidation catalysts and the high platinum binary alloys may be used for hot cathodes in special amplifiers.

COPPER PLATINUM

The system platinum copper, which comprises a continuous series of solid solutions above about 800°C, transforms at lower temperatures yielding the ordered phases based upon PtCu and $PtCu_3$. The liquidus and solidus, determined by Doerinckel (99), lie close together and descend smoothly from the melting point of platinum to that of copper.

Sedstrom (106), Johansson and Linde (107), Kurnakow and Nemilow (108) and Linde (174) investigated the system by means of resistance measurements, thermal analysis and X-ray determinations of the lattice structure and established the existence of the low temperature phases based on PtCu (24.5% copper) and $PtCu_3$ (49.41% copper). The diagram in its present state is shown in Figure 16.

The exact limits of the low temperature phases are as yet unknown. The transformation based on Pt Cu was evident in the thermal analysis curves of Kurnakow and Nemilow and begins at about 800°C and 25% copper broadening with fall in temperature. From Linde's (174) resistance measurements, it appears that this phase extends over the range 5 to 35% copper at low temperatures. The fact that Wise (109) obtained a considerable increase in tensile strength by heat treating the cold worked 4.5% copper alloy and only a slight increase in the 3% copper alloy also indicates that this transformation extends to at least 4.5% copper. According to Nowack (90), the alloys containing about 25% copper precipitation harden considerably. Linde (174) found that in the compound CuPt, which has trigonal symmetry, the excess platinum atoms assume an ordered arrangement when the copper content is less than 24.5%.

The transformation based on Cu_3Pt is not evident in the thermal analysis curves but from resistance measurements it is believed to begin at about 500°C and 50% copper broadening unsymmetrically to extend from about 48 to 75% copper at 400°C. Transformed alloys in this range retain the face centered cubic lattice but develop an ordered arrangement of atoms. Only

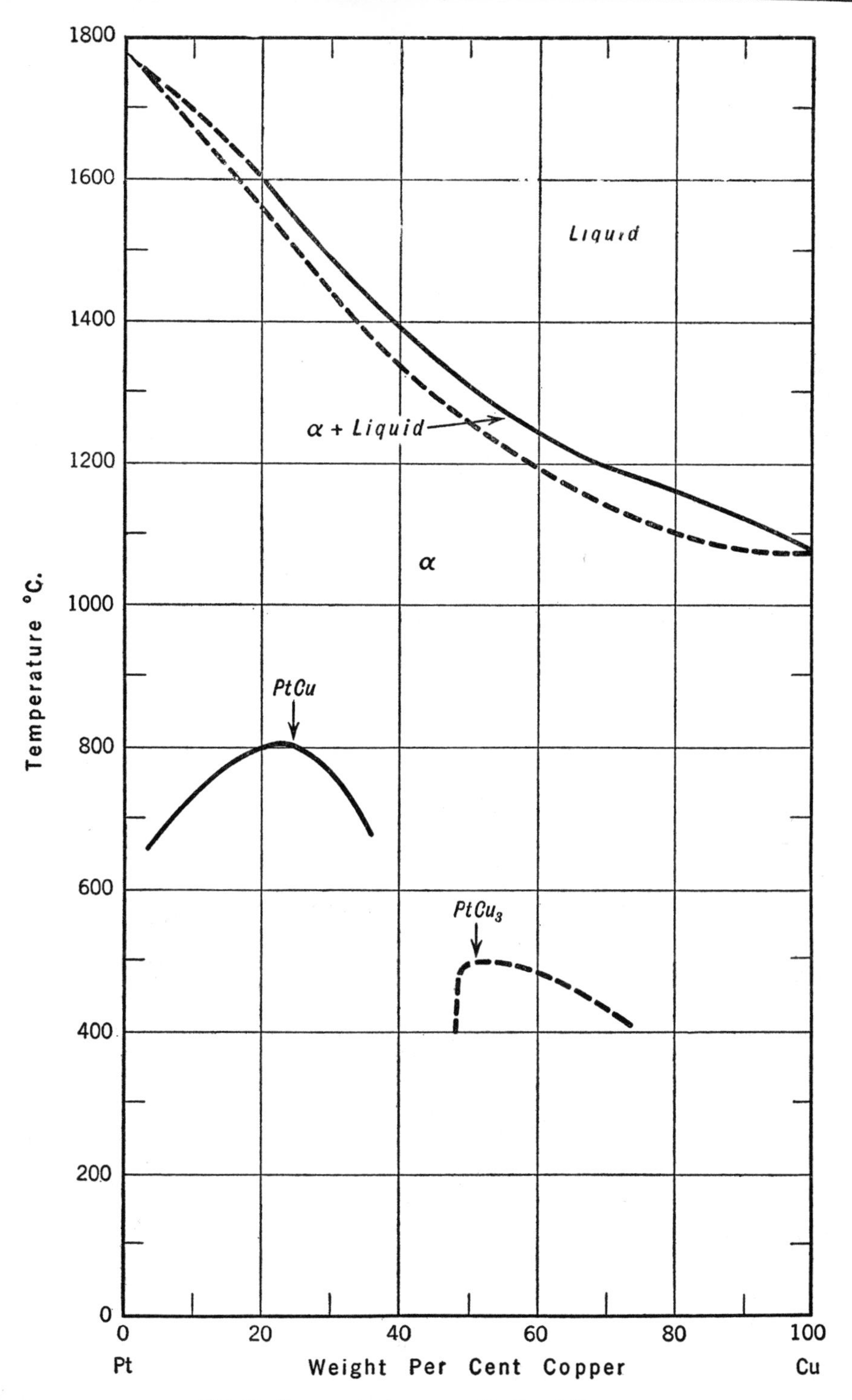

Fig. 16. *Copper-platinum constitutional diagram.*

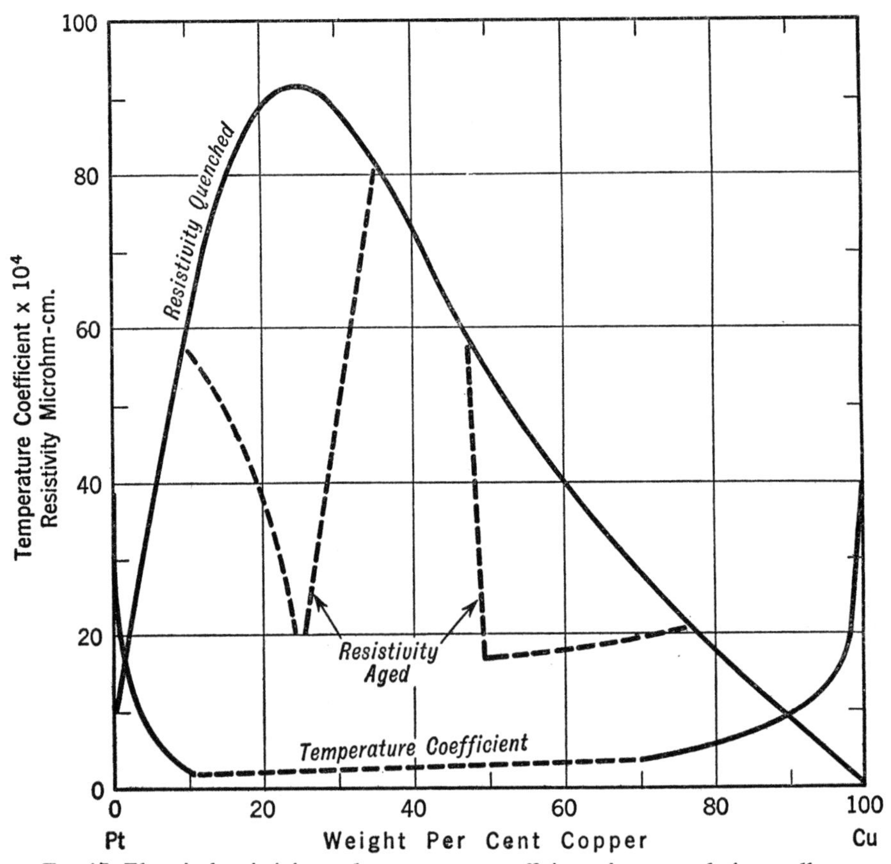

FIG. 17. *Electrical resistivity and temperature coefficient of copper-platinum alloys.*

mild precipitation hardening occurs in the 50 percent copper alloy.

ELECTRICAL PROPERTIES

The electrical resistivity of this series has been investigated by Sedstrom (106), Johansson and Linde (107), Kurnakow and Nemilow (108) and Linde (174) with fairly consistent results. According to Sedstrom, the maximum resistivity of about 92 microhm-cm for the solid solution alloys occurs at about 25% copper as shown in Figure 17. He also found minimum resistivities of about 20 and 17 microhm-cm for the aged alloys at about 25 and 50% copper respectively. Linde (174) in more recent measurements found minimum resistivities of 10.15 and 12.2 microhm-cm at 24 and 54% copper, respectively, for alloys quenched and tempered at 300°C. Naturally the resistivity of the aged alloys will vary with heat treatment. The temperature coefficient of electrical resistance for the solid solution alloys is also shown in Figure 17.

MECHANICAL PROPERTIES

The mechanical properties of this series of alloys have not been extensively investigated. Kurnakow and Nemilow (108) determined the hardness of the whole series of alloys in both the quenched and slowly cooled conditions but their values appear to be low, perhaps due to the use of very long anneals. Carter (17) measured the hardness of alloys containing up to 20%

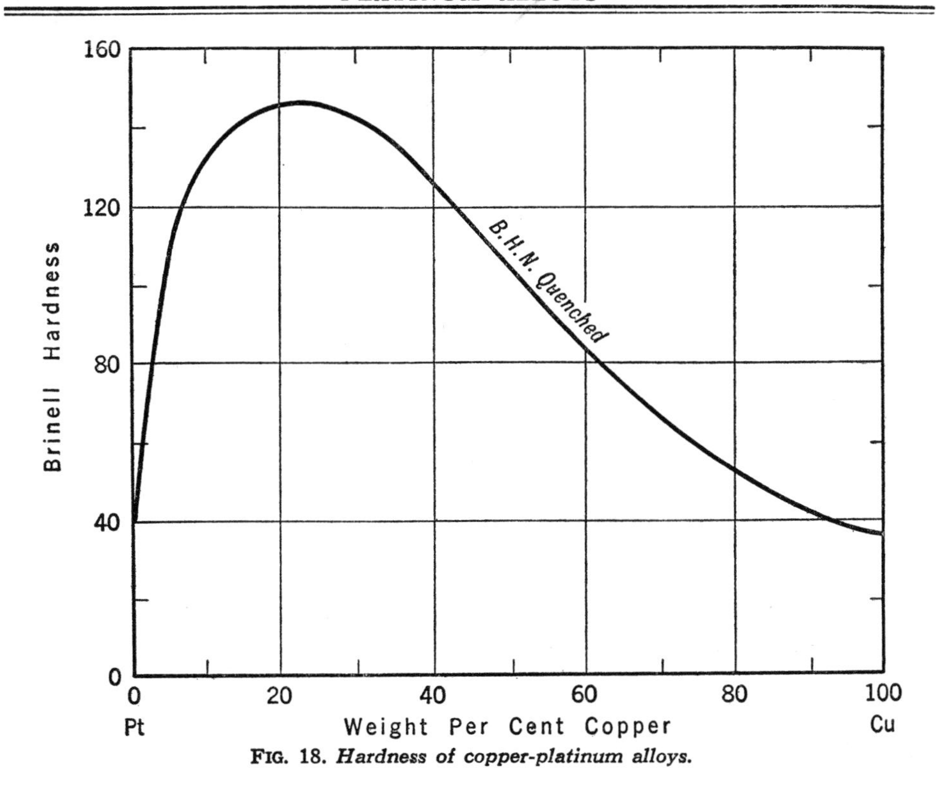

FIG. 18. *Hardness of copper-platinum alloys.*

copper and these are in agreement with those of Nowack (90) on alloys in the vicinity of 25% copper. Averaged values shown in Figure 18 indicate a maximum hardness of about 145 BHN at about 25% copper for annealed alloys. According to Nowack (90), the hardness of alloys containing about 25% copper can be more than doubled by aging, while that of the 50% copper alloy is only slightly increased. However, Wise and Vines (173) obtained only slight hardening in previously annealed 5 to 20% copper alloys on aging at 450 to 550°C for 30 minutes.

Tensile properties of the low copper content alloys, as determined by Raper and Rhodes (170), are listed in Table 35.

Cold worked alloys containing more than about 4% copper can be further hardened by heat treatment but such

TABLE 35
Tensile Properties of Copper Platinum Alloys

% Copper	Tensile Strength Lbs. per sq. in.		Proportional Limit Lbs. per sq. in.		Elongation % in 2"	
	Hard	Annealed	Hard	Annealed	Hard	Annealed
0	36000	22000	27000	5300	2.5	34
4.5	81000	53900	58600	12000	1.5	26
10.0	118700	79400	84100	19400	3	32

treatment is relatively ineffective on annealed alloys. For the 4.5% copper alloy, cold drawn 50%, aging for 10 minutes at 450°C increased the tensile strength from 81,000 to 98,000 lbs. per sq. in. and the proportional limit from 58,600 to 85,000 lbs. per sq. in.

WORKABILITY

The intermediate alloys require quenching from the solid solution domain to increase the ductility and make them amenable to working. Carter (17) reports that the alloys with up to 30% copper can be hot worked.

CORROSION AND TARNISH RESISTANCE

According to Carter (17) alloys containing less than 10% copper do not blacken on heating in air, but above this content copper is selectively oxidized yielding a blackened surface. He also reports that the 50% copper alloy is resistant to nitric acid.

USES

The 3 and 4.5% copper alloys are used for hard jewelry alloys in Europe. Low copper content platinum contacts show low weight loss and remain smooth in high tension magneto service, but have a higher contact resistance than the palladium platinum or iridium platinum alloys.

GOLD PLATINUM

Doerinckel (99), with the aid of cooling curves determined the liquidus and approximate solidus of platinum gold alloys in the range 40 to 100% gold and concluded that an uninterrupted series of solid solutions crystallize from platinum gold melts, although the spread between the liquidus and solidus is unusually large. Repeating the thermal analysis, Grigoriev (100) reported results in radical disagreement with those of Doerinckel. Later, Johansson and Linde (101) studied the system by means of X-ray, electrical resistance, thermal conductivity, hardness and magnetic susceptibility measurements and confirmed the type diagram proposed by Doerinckel.

Based upon the work of these investigators, mainly that of Johansson and Linde, it is now concluded that a continuous series of solid solutions exists at high temperature, but that below about 1150°C the mutual solubility drops, as shown in Figure 19. Within this immiscibility gap, which extends from about 3.5 to 75% gold at 700°C according to Stenzel and Weerts (102), the solid solution, stable at higher temperatures, breaks down into two components, one consisting of gold saturated with platinum and the other of platinum saturated with gold, a behavior similar to that observed in the gold nickel system. Other intermediate phases with ordered atomic arrangements are believed to exist below about 600°C but the nature of these complex transformations is still obscure.

ELECTRICAL PROPERTIES

The electrical resistivities of the single phase alloys (quenched from a temperature above the heterogeneous domain) and of the duplex alloys (slowly cooled from 1000° to 400°C) according to Johansson and Linde (101), are shown in Figure 20. The resistivity of the single phase alloys reaches a rather flat maximum of about 43.5 microhm-cm at about 50% gold. For the duplex alloys, the resistivity will, of course, vary with heat treatment. Geibel's (87) values for the temperature coefficient of electrical resistance, over the range 0-160°C, for the gold rich alloys are also shown in the same figure.

MECHANICAL PROPERTIES

The heterogeneous domain probably extends from about 3 to 85% gold at low temperatures and the mechanical properties of alloys within this compositional domain depend greatly upon the heat treatment. The hardness of the single phase alloys (quenched from

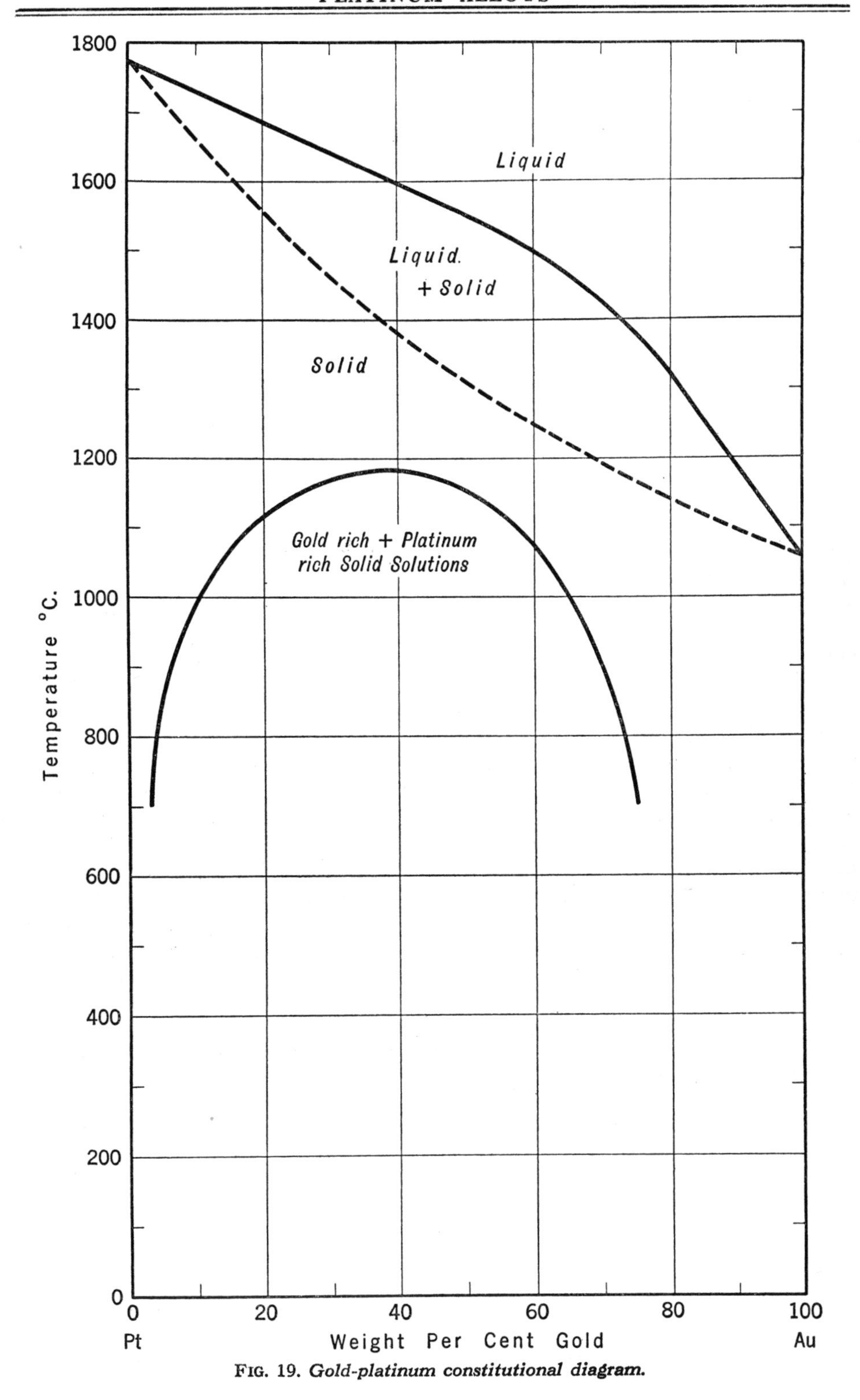

FIG. 19. *Gold-platinum constitutional diagram.*

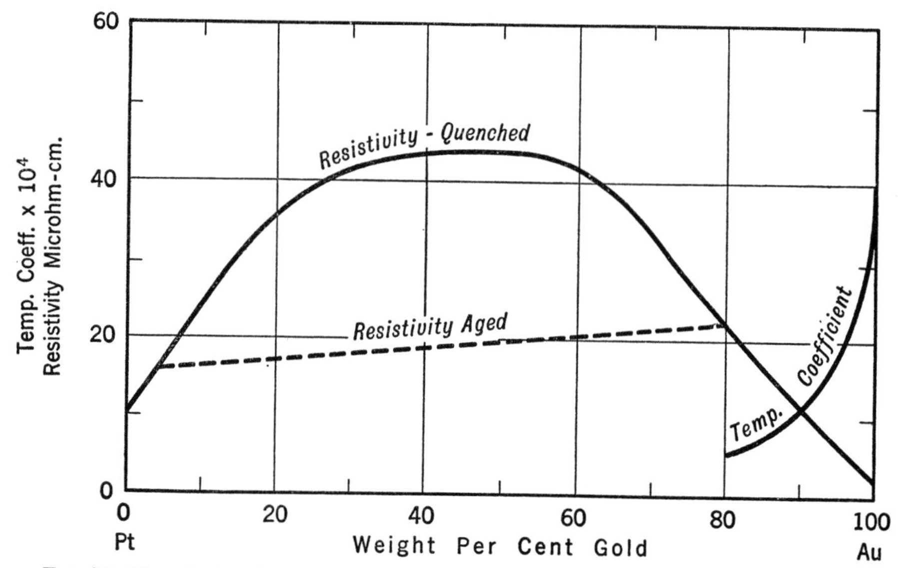

FIG. 20. *Electrical resistivity and temperature coefficient of gold-platinum alloys.*

a temperature above the heterogeneous domain) reaches a maximum of about 320 BHN at 25 to 35% gold according to Johansson and Linde (101). However, as pointed out by Wise and Crowell (103), it is probable that this rather high hardness is due in part to precipitation hardening occurring during quenching. These alloys can be further hardened to a maximum of 440 BHN at 25 to 35% gold by aging at temperatures in the neighborhood of 400°C. When quenched from a temperature within the heterogeneous domain, but above about 650°C, the resulting two phase alloys have a rather low hardness, the maximum being about 135 BHN at 20% gold as shown in Figure 21.

Tensile properties of some gold platinum alloys in the hard worked (50% reduction) and annealed conditions (65 and 172) are given in Table 36. Alloys within the heterogeneous field are susceptible to age hardening which results in an appreciable increase in tensile strength and proportional limit.

TABLE 36
Tensile Properties of Platinum-Gold Alloys

% Gold	Tensile Strength Lbs. per sq. in.		Proportional Limit Lbs. per sq. in.		Elongation % in 2"		Brinell Hardness	
	Hard	Annealed	Hard	Annealed	Hard	Annealed	Hard	Annealed
0	30000	19000	18000	low	4.5	37.5	80	40
2.5	49000	31000	38000	7500	2.5	26.5	138	70
5	63500	45000	40500	13000	2.0	23.0	155	92
7.5	79000	58500	45500	23000	1.25	15.0	187	123
10	90000	77500	63500	46000	1.25	12.5	222	143
60	.....	77000	.....	.....	....	....	225	175
70	.....	65000	.....	.....	....	....	195	135
80	.....	58000	.....	.....	....	....	160	105
90	.....	36000	.....	.....	....	....	105	60

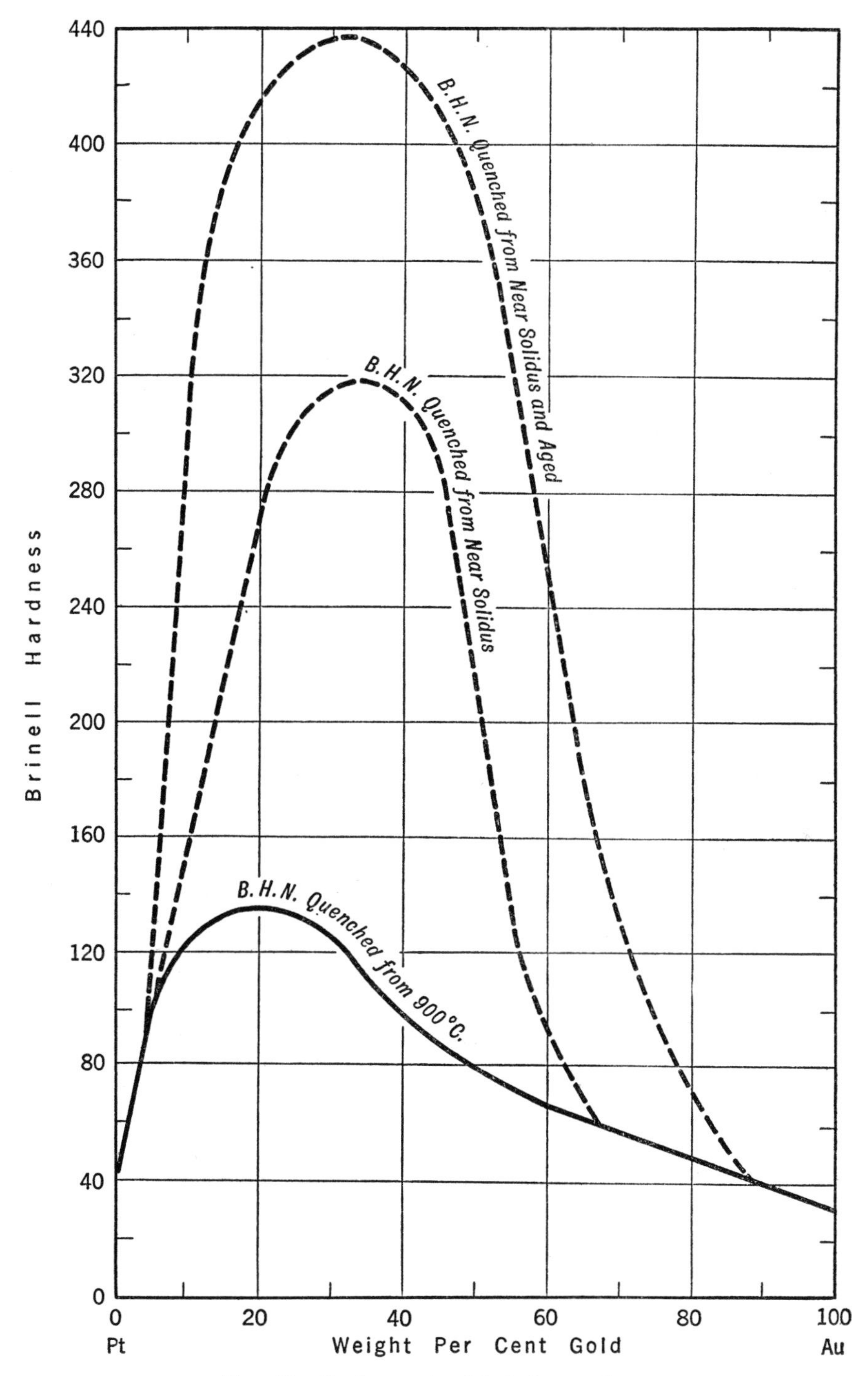

Fig. 21. *Hardness of gold-platinum alloys.*

Upon aging, the cold worked alloys show greater hardening than annealed and quenched alloys.

WORKABILITY

Although many of the platinum gold alloys are somewhat difficult to work, the entire series can be wrought after heat treating at 800-900°C followed by quenching. The gold-rich alloys are easier to work, but the coring developed during casting is very persistent.

COLOR

Alloys containing up to 70% gold are white if quenched from a sufficiently high temperature. Above 70% gold, the color ranges from a rather pale yellowish white to the yellow of pure gold.

CORROSION AND TARNISH RESISTANCE

The corrosion and tarnish resistance of these alloys is, of course, very high. In general, the homogeneous alloys are somewhat better than the two phase alloys of the same composition.

USES

Due to its high corrosion resistance and good mechanical properties, the 70% gold alloy is widely used for spinnerets in rayon production. However, rhodium platinum and platinum palladium gold alloys offer advantages and have found considerable use in replacing the simple platinum gold alloy, depending somewhat upon the relative prices of the platinum metals involved. Various platinum gold base alloys are also used for high melting point platinum solders.

IRIDIUM PLATINUM

The approximate liquidus of the platinum iridium system, after Feussner and Muller (89), modified to conform to later determinations of the melting point of iridium, is shown in Figure 22. The solidus has not been determined but is believed to lie close to the liquidus throughout.

Although this system has not been adequately investigated, it is believed to comprise a continuous series of solid solutions at high temperatures. However, as pointed out by Nowack (90), the increase in tensile strength obtained by heat treatment of cold worked platinum-rich alloys is evidence against the existence of a continuous series of solid solutions at low temperatures. Confirmation of a transformation in the face centered cubic solid solution was obtained in a recent study of the effect of quenching temperature on the resistivity and tensile strength of the 10 to 40% iridium alloys. The exact nature of the transformation has not been established but X-ray evidence indicates that it involves ordering rather than precipitation of a second phase. The investigators, Masing, Eckhardt and Kloiber (217), found the transformation temperature to increase smoothly from 780°C at 10% iridium to 940°C at 40% iridium. The transformation, which is somewhat sluggish and requires relatively long heat treatments to develop, results in a decrease in electrical resistivity and an increase in the tensile strength.

ELECTRICAL PROPERTIES

The electrical resistivity of the platinum rich alloys, after Geibel (87), Carter (17) and Nemilow (62), is shown in Figure 23 from which it is evident that iridium rapidly increases the resistivity of platinum. At 35% iridium the resistivity is about 36 microhm-cm at 20°C. Resistivity values for the alloys richer in iridium have not been determined due to the difficulty in working these alloys.

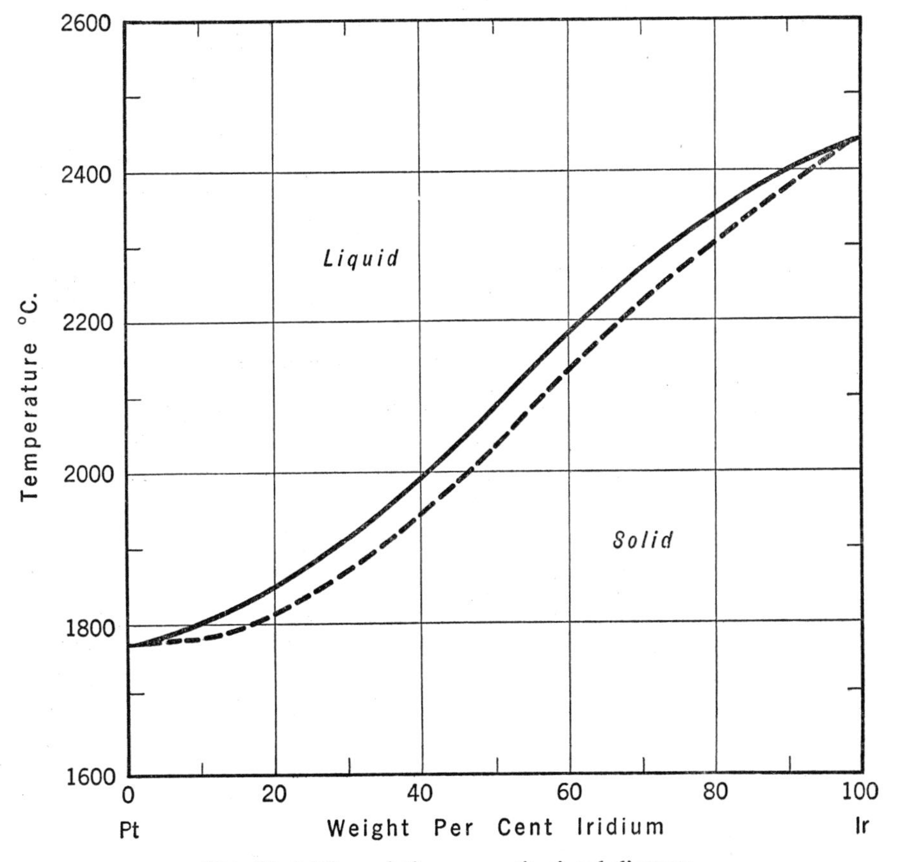

FIG. 22. *Iridium-platinum constitutional diagram.*

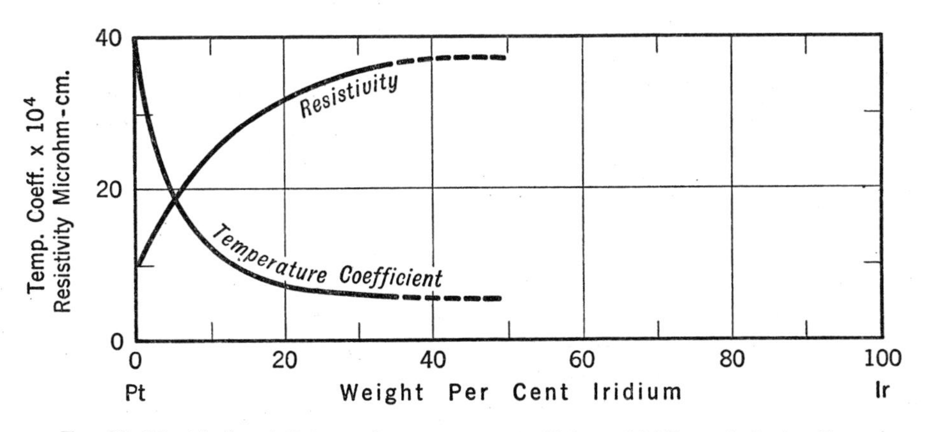

FIG. 23. *Electrical resistivity and temperature coefficient of iridium-platinum alloys.*

According to Masing, Eckhardt and Kloiber, the electrical resistivity of alloys in the range 10 to 40% iridium is dependent upon the heat treatment. The resistivity values given by these investigators appear to be in error, but there can be little doubt as to their observation that heating for long periods at low temperatures, or very slowly cooling from high temperatures, lowers the resistivity of alloys within this range.

The temperature coefficient of electrical resistance, after Geibel (87) and Carter (17), is shown in the same figure. At 35% iridium the temperature coefficient of electrical resistance is about 0.00058 per °C (0-100°C), according to these investigators. Nemilow (62) found that the temperature coefficient decreased gradually to a rather flat minimum at about 50% iridium.

MECHANICAL PROPERTIES

The Brinell hardness values of annealed alloys and cold worked platinum-rich alloys are shown in Figure 24. For the annealed alloys, the Brinell hardness reaches a maximum of about 250 BHN at about 50% iridium (62). These alloys require a rather high annealing temperature to completely soften them in a short time but somewhat higher hardnesses are obtained with normal commercial annealing treatments. Table 37. taken from Carter and Stauss (172), lists the mechanical properties of the commercially important platinum-rich platinum iridium alloys.

TABLE 37
Properties of Platinum-Iridium Alloys

% Ir	Brinell Hardness		Ultimate Tensile Strength Lbs. per sq. in.	
	Hard	Annealed	Hard	Annealed
0	97	42	34,000	18,000
5	140	90	70,000	40,000
10	185	130	90,000	55,000
15	230	160	120,000	75,000
20	265	200	145,000	100,000
25	310	240	170,000	125,000
30	360	280	200,000	160,000

The ultimate tensile strength values, based mainly on the work of Wise and Eash (27), for cold worked and annealed platinum-rich alloys are shown in Figure 24. For the 20% iridium alloy the tensile strength is 140,000 lbs. per sq. in. when cold worked (50% reduction) and 95,000 lbs. per sq. in. when annealed. According to Carter and Stauss (172), a tensile strength of 200,000 lbs. per sq. in. can be obtained in the cold worked 30% iridium alloy.

The alloys containing from 10 to 40% iridium can be mildly hardened by heat treatment. According to Geibel (87) and Steinmann (91), maximum tensile strengths are obtained in the 15 to 25% iridium alloys by heat treating the cold worked alloys at 750°C for one-half hour. Wise and Eash (27), obtained a maximum proportional limit in the cold worked 20% iridium alloy after heat treating for 5 minutes at 800°C. For annealed 10 to 30% iridium alloys, Masing et al (217) found that heating for 24 hours at about 550°C produced the greatest increase in tensile strength which amounted to about 10% in the 10% iridium alloy and 20% in the 25% iridium alloy.

WORKABILITY

The ductility of the alloys decreases with increase in iridium content and at about 35% iridium it drops so low that the alloys are very difficult to work. Alloys containing more than 10% iridium require rather high annealing temperatures, in the neighborhood of 1400°C to completely soften

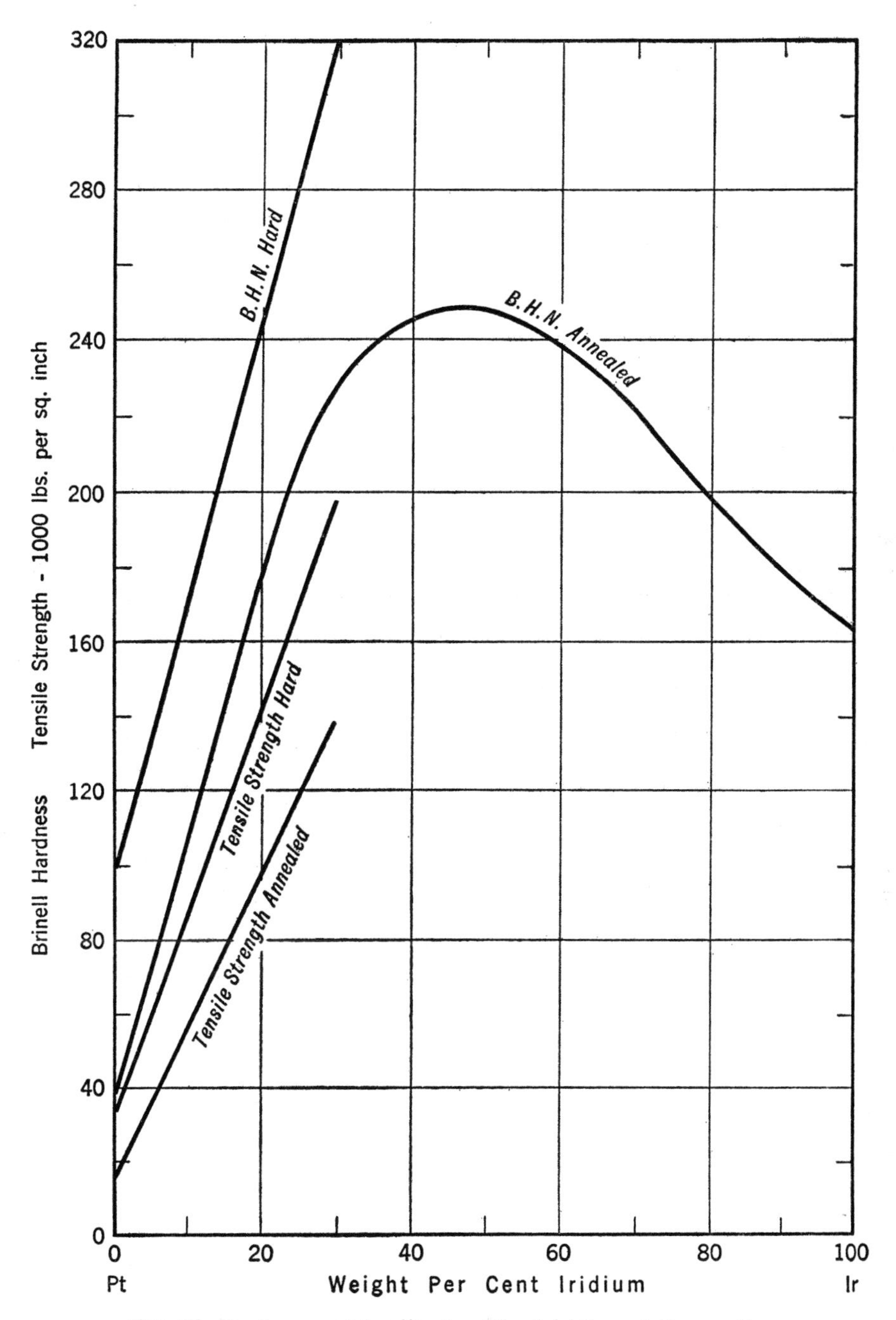

FIG. 24. *Hardness and tensile strength of iridium-platinum alloys.*

them in a short time, although in practice, anneals at about 1100 to 1200°C for 30 to 45 minutes are sometimes employed.

CORROSION AND TARNISH RESISTANCE

The corrosion and tarnish resistance of these alloys is excellent and with increasing iridium content the alloys become increasingly resistant to nascent chlorine and aqua regia. On heating above about 900°C in air, iridium platinum alloys lose weight due to oxidation and volatilization of iridium oxide, the loss in weight increasing with iridium content. At temperatures between 900 and 1150°C alloys containing more than about 5% iridium are darkened in air by a superficial oxide film, but at higher temperatures the oxide decomposes and the surface regains its color.

USES

The nobility, rich color and intrinsic value of platinum alloyed with from 5 to 15% iridium, depending upon the mechanical strength required, have made it the preferred metal for jewelry. Higher iridium content alloys, containing up to 25% iridium, are used for electrical contacts in magnetos, relays and thermostats which must give dependable service. The 10% iridium platinum alloy is employed for electrodes in electrochemical processes where chlorine or other potent corrosives are evolved. Platinum alloyed with 0.4 to 0.6% of iridium is commonly employed for crucibles, and other low iridium content alloys, of carefully controlled analysis, are used for safety bursting disks which must resist highly corrosive media. The 10 and 20% iridium alloys are also used for detonator fuse wires. Hypodermic needles, which can be flame sterilized without damage, are made from the 25 or 30% iridium alloys. The use of iridium platinum electrodes for aircraft spark plugs is proving of great importance. Recently the iridium platinum alloys containing a few percent of iridium and small amounts of nickel have been employed for bushings for sizing molten glass in the production of glass fiber and glass wool.

Because of their permanence, platinum iridium alloys have been selected for governmental standards of length and weight. Simulating natural teeth in appearance and function, porcelain covered cast platinum iridium restorations are becoming increasingly popular with prosthetic dentists. High strength corrosion resisting platinum iridium wires have also long been used by orthodontists.

IRON PLATINUM

According to Isaac and Tammann (114), the liquidus and solidus of this system fall quite rapidly up to about 30% iron and then very slowly to a minimum of about 1500°C between 80 and 90% iron. The temperature of the gamma to delta change in iron is increased by platinum so that alloys containing up to about 90 to 95% iron crystallize as a gamma face centered cubic solid solution. According to Graf and Kussmann (115), between 10 and 40% iron the gamma solid solution undergoes a transformation, based upon the compound FePt (22.2% iron), at temperatures below about 1100°C. This compound has an unordered body centered cubic lattice.

The Curie temperature (magnetic transformation) in the range of 10 to 40% iron depends upon the state of the alloy; being higher in the transformed state than in the quenched state as shown in Figure 25. In the range 43.5 to 100% iron, the temperature of the alpha-gamma transformation increases with increase in iron content. The gamma to alpha transformation on cooling increases from about 20°C at 43.5% iron to 915°C at 100% iron. For the reverse transformation on heating, the increase over the same range is from 580°C to 915°C. According to Kussmann (116), the alloys containing between 40 and 50% iron have a negative coefficient of thermal expansion which, over the range 20 to 70°C, shows the most highly negative value at about 45% iron.

ELECTRICAL PROPERTIES

Nemilow (117) determined the electrical resistivity of the iron-rich alloys and reported that the resistivity of quenched alloys at 25°C decreased from 41 microhm-cm at 63.8% iron to 13.32 microhm-cm for pure iron. Slowly cooled alloys had similar resistivities. He also determined the temperature coefficient of electrical resistance for the entire series of alloys and found that between 15 and 30% iron the temperature coefficient of the slowly cooled alloys was higher than that of the quenched alloys, which is presumably a reflection of the FePt transformation in this range. The 21% iron alloy had a temperature coefficient, over the range 25 to 100°C, of 0.0008 per °C when quenched and 0.0041 per °C when slowly cooled.

MAGNETIC PROPERTIES

The high coercive forces of the 15 to 34% iron alloys in the quenched state are shown in Figure 26 which records the data collected by Graf and Kussmann (115) on these alloys after quenching from 1100°C or slowly cooling. From this figure, it is evident that the maximum in the coercive force occurs at about 22.2% (50 atomic percent) iron. According to these investigators, in the 21.5% iron alloy, the coercive force is 1540 oersteds after quenching from 1100°C and 316 oersteds after slow cooling. However, in view of Gebhardt and Kosters (216) work on the cobalt platinum alloys and the general similarity of the systems, it is probable that even better magnetic properties might be obtained in the iron platinum alloys by judicious heat treatment of the quenched alloys. Aging in a magnetic field would also appear desirable.

The magnetic characteristics of the quenched 22.2% iron alloy as reported by Neumann (218) are shown in Figure 27. According to Graf and Kussmann, this alloy had a coercive force of 1570 oersteds, a residual induction of 5830 gausses and an energy product $(BH)_{max.}$ of 3,070,000. Saturation values for the series of alloys, after Graf and Kussmann, are shown in Figure 28.

MECHANICAL PROPERTIES

Nemilow (117) investigated the hardness of the entire series of alloys in both the quenched and slowly cooled conditions with results as shown in Figure 29. In the annealed condition hardness maxima of about 150 BHN and 145 BHN occur at 22.5% iron and 73% iron respectively. Age hardening occurs on slow cooling the alloys in the range 10 to 70% iron, the maximum hardening apparently occurring at about 30% iron. This hardening may be attributed to the FePt transformation in alloys containing 10 to 40% iron but the reason for the observed hardening in the range 40 to 70% iron is not evident. The abrupt break in the hardness curve of the slowly cooled alloys and the low hardness of the 22.5% iron alloy are probably due to over-aging.

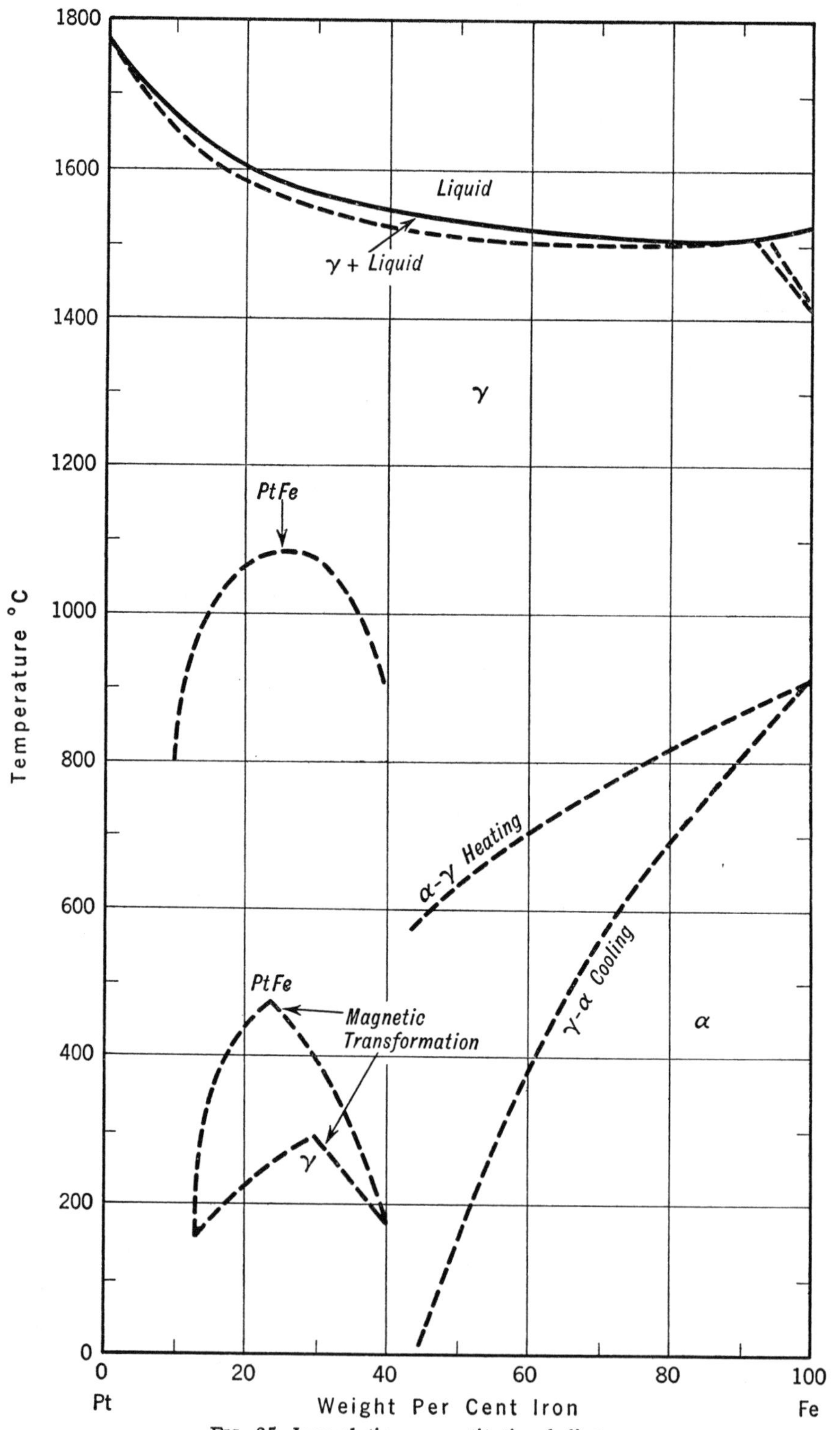

FIG. 25. *Iron-platinum constitutional diagram.*

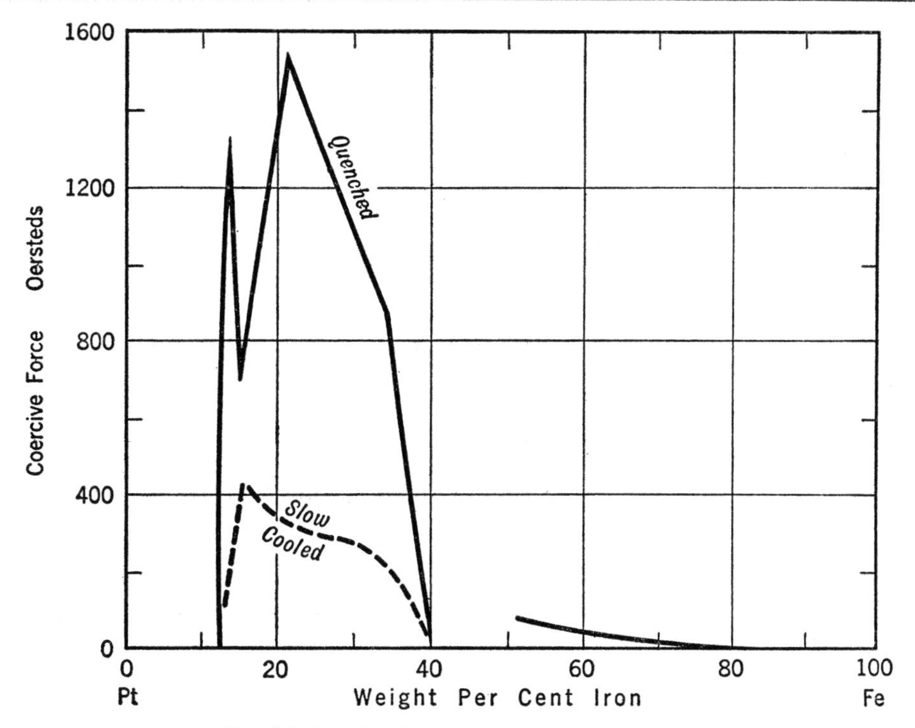

FIG. 26. *Coercive force of iron-platinum alloys.*

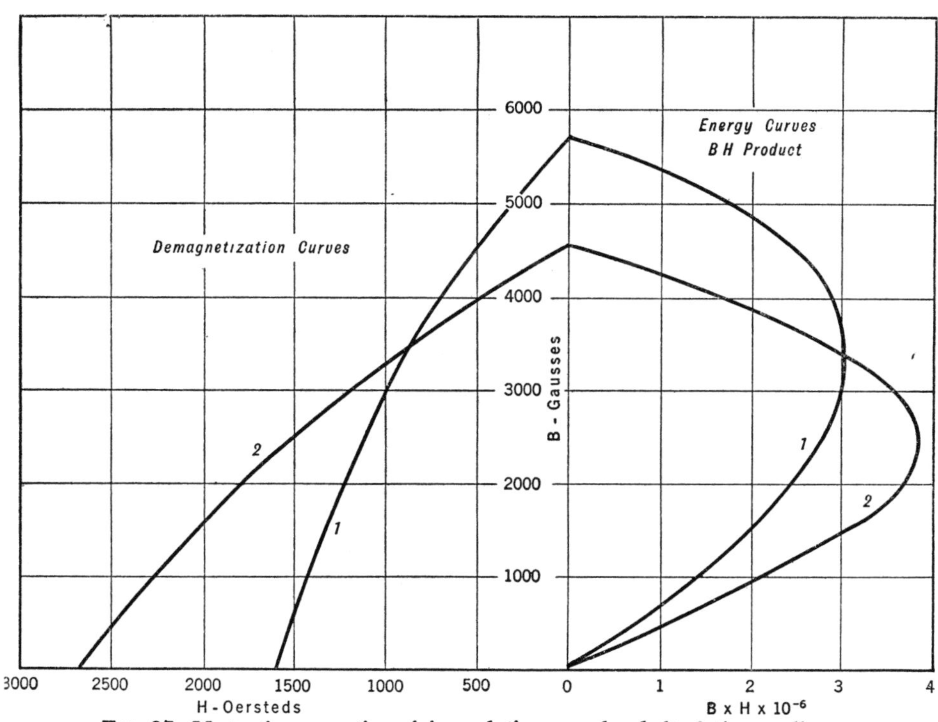

FIG. 27. ***Magnetic properties of iron-platinum and cobalt-platinum alloys:***
1. 22.2% *iron,* 77.8% *platinum.*
2. 23.3% *cobalt,* 76.7% *platinum.*

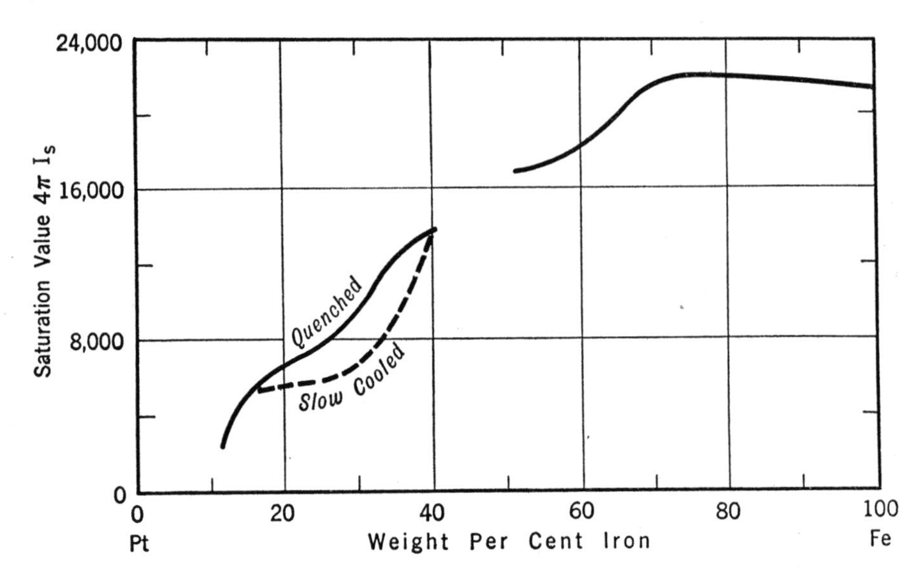

FIG. 28. ***Magnetic saturation values of iron-platinum alloys.***

USES

The 22.2% iron alloy is characterized by extraordinary permanent magnet qualities which may lead to application of this and the still better cobalt platinum alloy where minimum dimensions are essential. The alloys of low or negative thermal expansivity may also find application in small instruments. The thermoelastic properties of the iron and cobalt platinum alloys also appear to be worth investigating with the possibility of using them for hair springs in watches and fine scientific instruments.

LEAD PLATINUM

According to Doerinckel (125), the addition of lead to platinum rapidly lowers the liquidus temperature from the melting point of platinum to about 915°C at 42% lead. In the platinum-rich alloys, two compounds are formed by peritectic reactions, Pt_3Pb (26% lead) at 915°C and PtPb (52% lead) at 795°C. Zintl and Kaiser (179) found that the compound PtPb has a nickel arsenide structure. The solid solubility of lead in platinum has not been determined but is believed to be quite low.

ELECTRICAL PROPERTIES

According to Carter (51) an 0.1% Pb alloy has an electrical resistivity of 12.3 microhm-cm at 20°C and a temperature coefficient of resistance between 20° and 90°C of 0.00305 per °C. The emf of this alloy against platinum is 2.3 millivolts at 1200°C.

MECHANICAL PROPERTIES

Carter (51) found that platinum-rich alloys containing 1% or more of lead were not workable but that an alloy containing 0.1% lead was sufficiently ductile to be worked into wire. This 0.1% lead alloy had a tensile strength of 48,000 lbs. per sq. in. in the annealed condition.

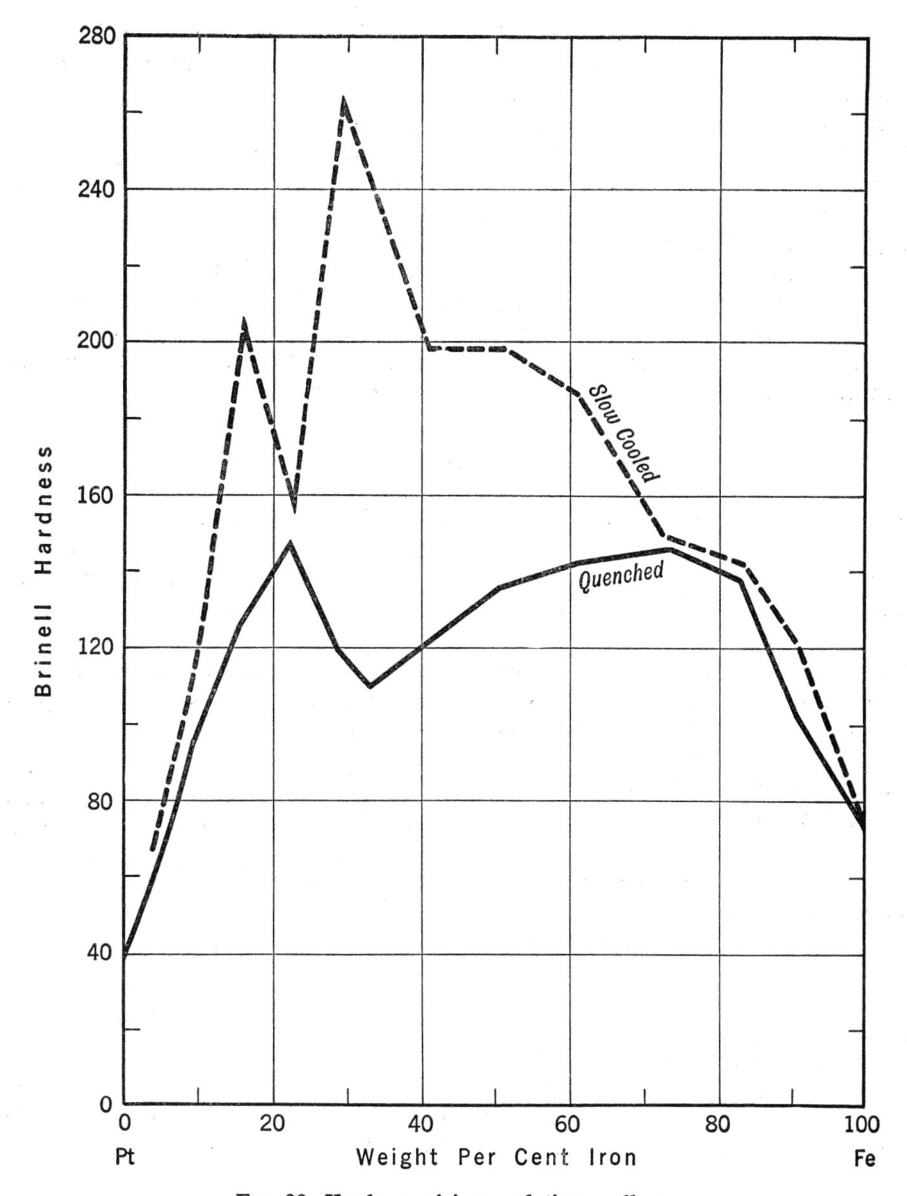

FIG. 29. *Hardness of iron—platinum alloys.*

MAGNESIUM PLATINUM

Platinum melted in magnesia under reducing conditions is difficult to work, which indicates that magnesium forms a low melting or brittle compound with platinum. Carter (199) obtained platinum containing as much as 3% magnesium by melting in a magnesia crucible under reducing conditions.

MANGANESE PLATINUM

According to Nemilow, Vidusova and Pivovarova (178) the liquidus of this system reaches a minimum at about 45% manganese. Heat effects are obtained at 22% manganese (PtMn) and 956°C and 53% manganese ($PtMn_4$) and 980°C, indicating the formation of these compounds or ordered phases from the solid solution. Another compound Pt_3Mn (8.5% manganese) is indicated from the hardness and temperature coefficient of resistance measurements. They also report that alloys containing up to 5% manganese are sufficiently ductile to be drawn into wire. With high purity manganese it is probable that this limit would be extended.

USES

Platinum-rich alloys might have some application in spark plug electrodes, electrical contacts and electrolytic and catalytic processes.

MOLYBDENUM PLATINUM

Nemilow and Voronow (119) investigated this system up to about 42% molybdenum and concluded from microscopic examination and hardness and resistance measurements that, up to the maximum molybdenum content studied, the system comprises an uninterrupted series of solid solutions. The possibility of low temperature transformations has, however, not been adequately investigated.

ELECTRICAL RESISTIVITY

The electrical resistivity and temperature coefficient of electrical resistance of the 2.2% molybdenum alloy are reported as 31.5 microhm-cm at 25°C and 0.00101 per °C over the range 25-100°C respectively (119). Platinum molybdenum alloys develop high thermoelectric forces against platinum, 21.70 millivolts at 1000°C for the 2.2% molybdenum alloy, but due to the selective oxidation of molybdenum, they are not useful for thermocouple elements.

MECHANICAL PROPERTIES

According to Nemilow and Voronow (119), the hardness of the 2.2% molybdenum alloy is 77 BHN. Wise and Vines (173) found the hardness of a 2.5% molybdenum platinum alloy to be 117 VHN when annealed at 1100°C and 210 VHN after cold rolling 50%.

USES

Hard, brittle, complex platinum molybdenum base alloys have been used for fountain pen tipping materials because of their corrosion and abrasion resistance. The binary alloys may also find some use as electrical contacts.

NICKEL PLATINUM

Based upon the works of Kurnakow and Nemilow (110) and Kussmann and Nitka (175), it is now believed that the system platinum nickel comprises a continuous series of solid solutions above about 600°C. Up to about 30% nickel, the addition of nickel to platinum results in rapid lowering of the liquidus but thereafter the liquidus remains almost horizontal as shown in Figure 30. Present evidence indicates that the solidus remains close to the liquidus throughout.

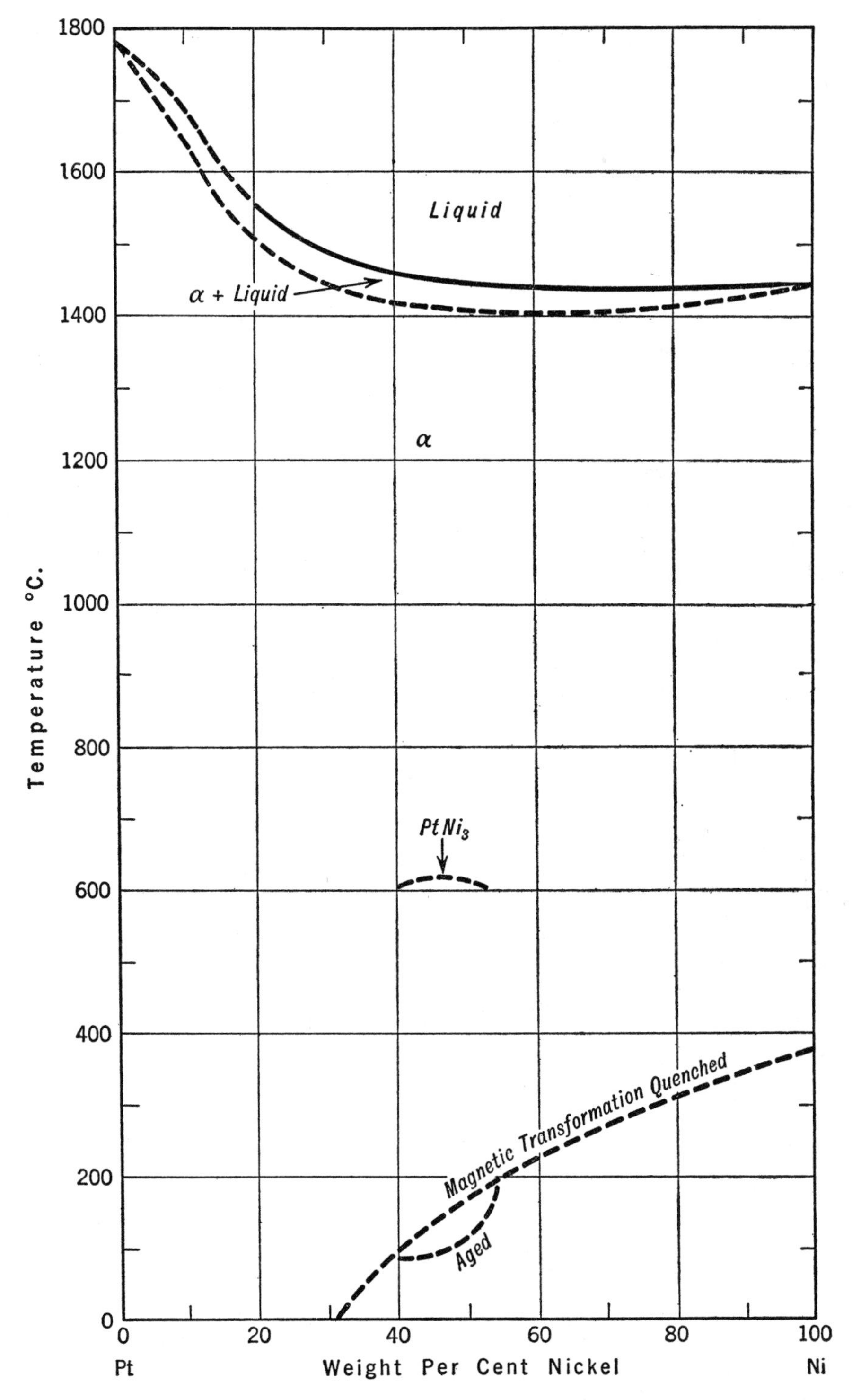

FIG. 30. *Nickel-platinum constitutional diagram.*

Kussmann and Nitka, who studied the system by means of X-ray, magnetic and electrical methods, concluded that a superstructure based on Ni_3Pt forms at about 600°C over the range 40 to 53% nickel. It is possible that another transformation involving NiPt occurs at about 23% nickel, but evidence concerning this has not been reported. In the solid solution alloys, the temperature of the magnetic change, which occurs at about 0°C in the 32% nickel alloy, increases smoothly with the nickel content to 368°C for nickel.

The development of the ordered state reduces the Curie temperature and the electrical resistivity.

ELECTRICAL PROPERTIES

The electrical resistivity (176) and the temperature coefficient of electrical resistance (110) of the platinum nickel alloys are shown in Figure 31. A maximum resistivity of about 42 microhm-cm at 30% nickel is indicated for the solid solution alloys. The transformed alloys have a slightly lower resistivity. A minimum temperature coefficient of electrical resistance of about 0.00075 per °C (25-100°C) at about 23% (50 atomic percent) nickel has been reported.

MECHANICAL PROPERTIES

Nickel rapidly hardens platinum, a rather sharp maximum of about 250 BHN occurring at 23% (50 atomic percent) nickel for the annealed alloys as shown in Figure 32. According to Wise and Eash (27) the tensile strength of the 5% nickel alloy is 65,000 lbs. per sq. in. annealed and 103,500 lbs. per sq. in. cold worked (50% reduction).

WORKABILITY

All except the very hard alloys are easily worked.

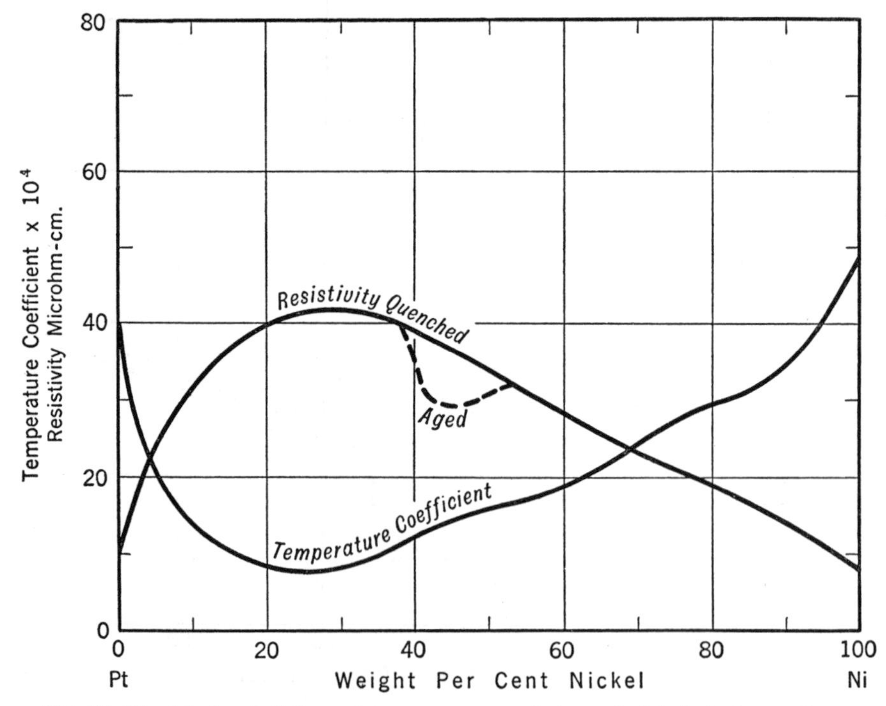

FIG. 31. *Electrical resistivity and temperature coefficient of nickel-platinum alloys.*

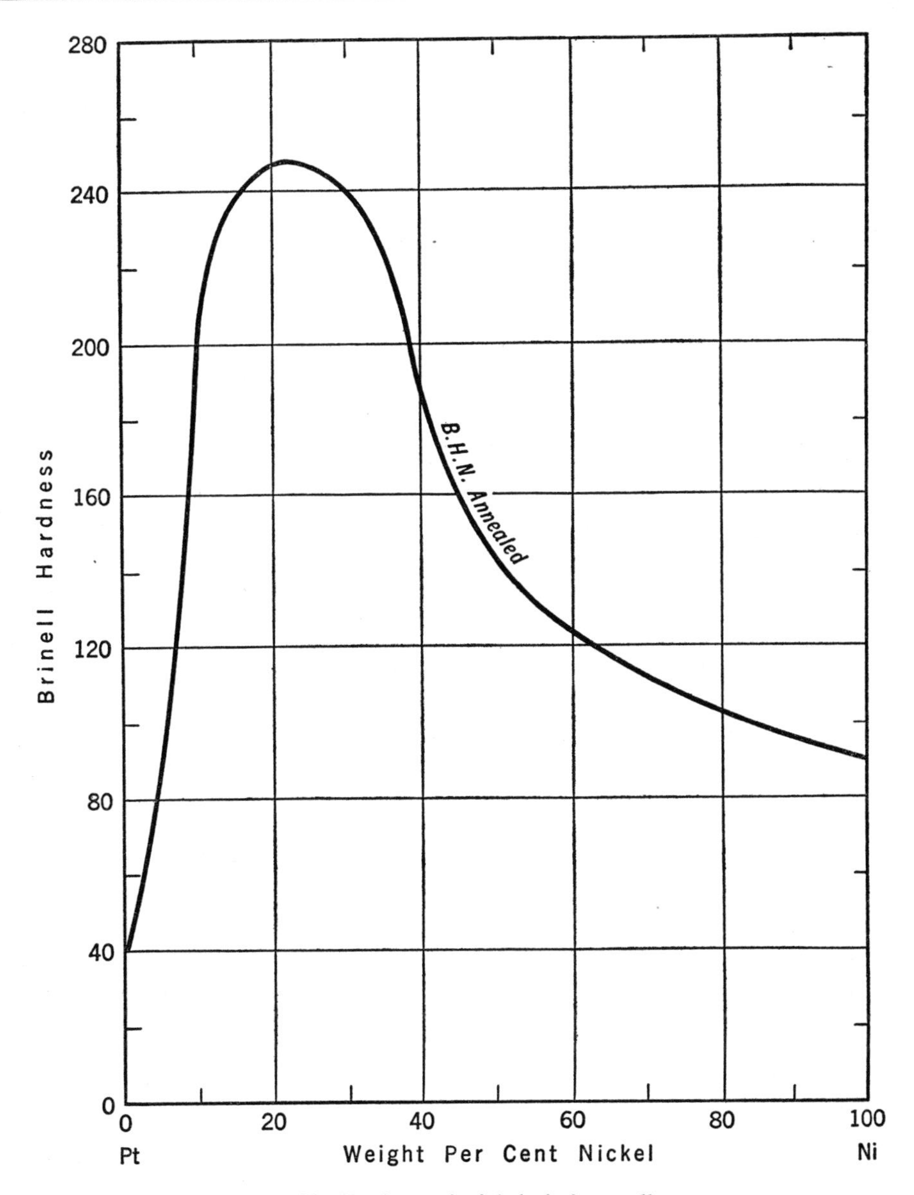

Fig. 32. ***Hardness of nickel-platinum alloys.***

CORROSION AND TARNISH RESISTANCE The addition of platinum to nickel does not rapidly increase the nobility. As measured by the drop test, approximately 40% platinum is required to yield nitric acid resistance comparable to 14 Kt. jewelry gold, and 50% platinum is required to yield complete resistance in this test. About 55% platinum is required to obtain a resistance to ferric chloride, and freedom from tarnish by industrial atmospheres, which will be equal to that of 14 Kt. jewelry gold. Higher platinum content alloys are, of course, quite resistant to corrosion and tarnish.

COLOR

The color of platinum nickel alloys is intermediate between the colors of the end members.

USES

The 95% platinum, 5% nickel alloy has been used as the core in long life barium-strontium oxide coated thermionic cathodes and affords not only a good cathode base but retains its strength exceptionally well at high temperatures.

OSMIUM PLATINUM

This system has not been investigated, but from the high hardness and low ductility of the alloys containing more than about 10% of osmium and the fact that the metals belong to different crystallographic systems, it is believed that an intermetallic compound or an ordered phase is formed.

ELECTRICAL PROPERTIES

The electrical resistivity of the 5% osmium alloy is about 24 microhm-cm at 20°C and for the 10% osmium alloy, it is about 33 microhm-cm at 20°C.

MECHANICAL PROPERTIES

For the Brinell hardness of the annealed 5 and 10% osmium alloys, Carter (17) gives 120 and 175 BHN respectively. Tensile properties of this system have not been reported.

CORROSION AND TARNISH RESISTANCE

Workable platinum-rich alloys have the chemical properties of platinum, but when heated under oxidizing conditions, appreciable loss of osmium as volatile osmium oxide is to be expected.

WORKABILITY

Alloys containing more than about 10% of osmium are very difficult to work. When annealing these alloys, the use of a non-oxidizing atmosphere is desirable, to prevent oxidation and subsequent volatilization of osmium, and because of the poisonous nature of osmium oxide, melting operations must be conducted under a fumehood.

USES

The simple binary alloys find relatively little use, but ternary and more complex osmium platinum base alloys find use for electrical contacts; for hard, cast or sintered sparking points, and for corrosion and abrasion resisting tips for pen nibs and long life phonograph needles.

PALLADIUM PLATINUM

The equilibrium relations in this system have not as yet been worked out, but it is believed that the liquidus and solidus lie close together and descend smoothly from the melting point of platinum to that of palladium.

Investigations of electrical resistivity by Carter (17), Geibel (87) and Schulze (88), temperature coefficient of resistance by Carter and Geibel, thermal conductivity by Schulze and magnetic susceptibility by Shimizu (46), indicate a continuous series of solid solutions devoid of transformation in the solid state. The mechanical properties also admit the same conclusion.

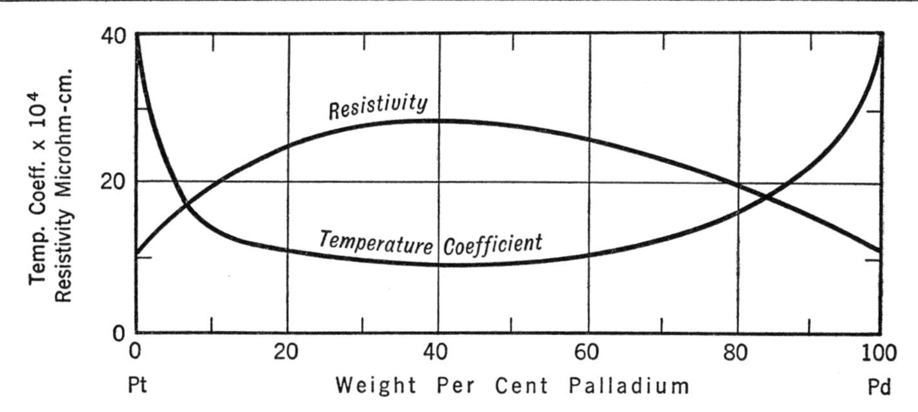

FIG. 33. *Electrical resistivity and temperature coefficient of palladium-platinum alloys.*

ELECTRICAL PROPERTIES

The electrical resistivity, based upon the findings of Carter, Geibel and Schulze, is shown in Figure 33. The resistivity reaches a maximum of 28.5 microhms-cm at 20°C for the alloy containing about 40% palladium. The temperature coefficient of electrical resistance, shown in the same figure, reaches a minimum of .00096 ohms per °C (0-160°C) at 40% palladium, according to Geibel.

MECHANICAL PROPERTIES

The Brinell hardness values, based mainly on the work of Carter (17), are shown in Figure 34. Maxima of about 100 BHN for the annealed alloy and 180 BHN for the cold worked alloy occur at about 40% palladium. According to Carter and Stauss (172), the tensile strength in the annealed condition attains a maximum of about 50,000 lbs. per sq. in. at 40% palladium.

WORKABILITY

All the alloys are very ductile and are easily worked.

CORROSION AND TARNISH RESISTANCE

Alloys containing up to 25% palladium have essentially the chemical properties of platinum and are not attacked by boiling nitric acid nor discolored by heating in air. In general, other alloys have chemical properties intermediate between those of the end members, but the addition of platinum to palladium rapidly increases the resistance to nitric acid. When tested by the drop test, a 2% platinum palladium alloy is as resistant to nitric acid as 14 Kt. jewelry gold, and the 10% platinum palladium alloy is completely resistant. Palladium-rich alloys darken when heated in air to temperatures between 400 and 800°C due to the superficial formation of palladium oxide which decomposes at higher temperatures, the surface again becoming bright.

USES

Trade requirements in the United States do not favor the use of platinum-rich platinum palladium alloys for jewelry, but alloys containing about 4% palladium are liked in Europe for difficult forming operations. Palladium-rich alloys containing minor amounts of platinum, usually in conjunction with iridium or ruthenium, have also been used for jewelry purposes in Europe. Palladium platinum electrical contacts containing 12% palladium remain smooth and show low weight loss in high tension magneto service.

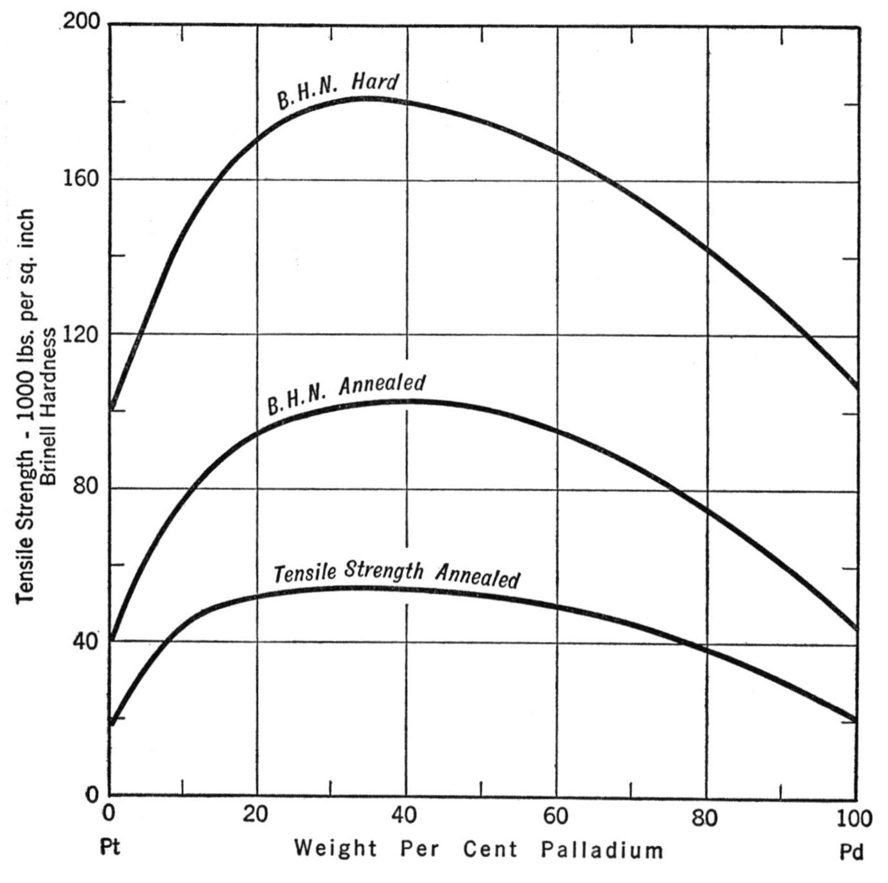

FIG. 34. *Hardness and tensile strength of palladium-platinum alloys.*

PHOSPHORUS PLATINUM

The liquidus of this system drops rapidly from the melting point of platinum to an eutectic at 588°C and 3.8% phosphorus according to Biltz, Weibke, May and Meisel (130). A subphosphide, $Pt_{20}P_7$ (5.27% phosphorus) is formed by a peritectic reaction at 590°C in melts with 3.8 to 24% phosphorus.

Between 5.3 and 14.7% phosphorus, there is a miscibility gap in the liquid state with a monotectic temperature at 683°C. The melting point of the compound PtP_2 (24% platinum) is above 1500°C. Jedele (131) determined the tensile strength and elongation of platinum containing small percentages of phosphorus at room temperature and at 850°C. His results show that even small amounts of phosphorus, less than 0.005%, markedly reduce the ductility at 850°C which indicates that the solid solubility of phosphorus in platinum is very low. Fischer (180) also found that traces of phosphorus in platinum crucibles lead to embrittlement due to the formation of the brittle fusible eutectic.

MECHANICAL PROPERTIES

Jedele (131) determined the mechanical properties of the low phosphorus content platinum alloys at room temperature and at 850°C with results as shown in Table 38.

Alloys containing more than 0.003% phosphorus were brittle at 850°C.

USES

Phosphorus was early used to lower the melting point of platinum to permit melting with equipment then available. After melting, the phosphorus was oxidized off. Phosphorus has also been added to complex platinum alloys to render them brittle so that they might be broken up to yield small grains used for tipping pen points.

TABLE 38
Mechanical Properties of Platinum-Phosphorus Alloys at Room Temperature and 850°C

	Room Temperature			850 °C.	
% Phosphorus	Brinell Hardness	Tensile Strength Lbs. per sq. in.	Elongation %	Tensile Strength Lbs. per sq. in.	Elongation %
0.96	145	......	...	......	...
0.26	75	36,800	4.75	......	...
0.105	60	33,400	11.3	......	...
0.025	53	30,400	19.4	......	...
0.005	50	29,700	11.9	......	...
0.003	50	19,800	14.2	6,000	6.2
0.001	45	21,200	24.9	11,200	6.1
.000	45	21,000	27.1	9,800	9.0

RHODIUM PLATINUM

The approximate liquidus-solidus temperatures for the platinum rhodium series have been determined by Acken (72) and Feussner and Muller (89). Acken measured temperatures with a brightness match optical pyrometer while Feussner and Muller used an optical pyrometer employing a photoelectric cell. The values reported by the latter investigators, when corrected in accordance with later determinations of the melting point of rhodium, agree quite well with those reported by Acken.

The temperatures shown in Figure 35 represent some point between the liquidus and the solidus since within the exactitude of the measurements, about 20°C, there was no perceptible

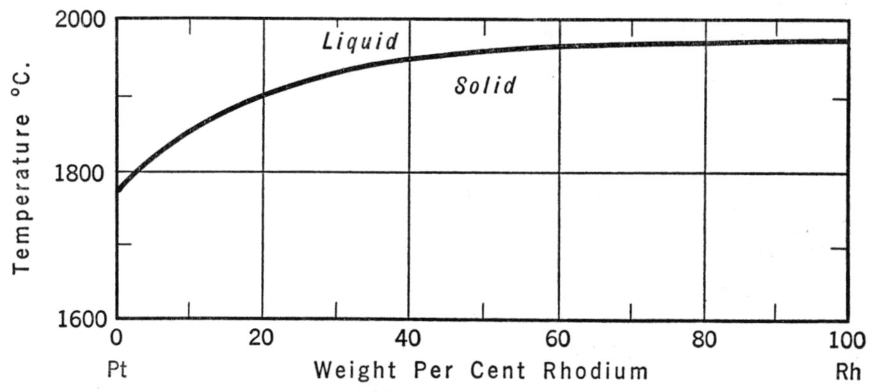

FIG. 35. *Approximate liquidus-solidus curve for the rhodium-platinum system.*

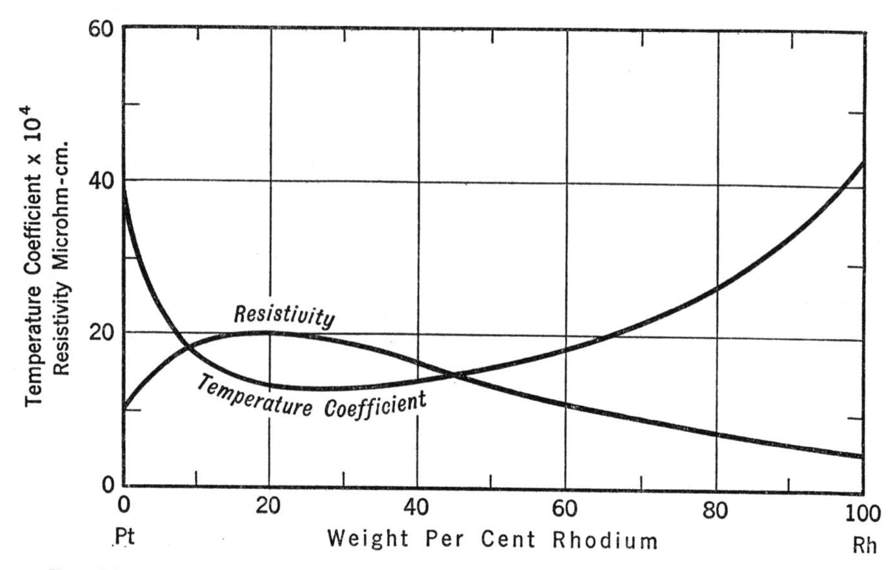

FIG. 36. *Electrical resistivity and temperature coefficient of rhodium-platinum alloys.*

difference between the two points. Hence, it is concluded that the liquidus and solidus lie close together throughout, ascending rapidly from the melting point of platinum to about 1950°C at 50% rhodium and then remaining almost constant with further increase in rhodium content.

From the electrical resistivity, the temperature coefficient of electrical resistivity and the Brinell hardness values of Acken (72) and Nemilow and Voronow (77), it is believed that a continuous series of solid solutions form on crystallization from platinum rhodium melts. However, the rather abrupt changes of slope in the curves of the thermal emf developed against pure platinum at temperatures below about 1000°C (Figure 37) suggest the possibility of transformations in the solid state. Hildebrand's (177) work on the magnetic susceptibility of the platinum-rich alloys also indicates the possible formation of an ordered $RhPt_3$ compound in the neighborhood of 15% rhodium but this is not evident in the thermal emf curves.

ELECTRICAL PROPERTIES

The electrical resistivity, based on values reported by Acken (72), Nemilow and Voronow (77) and Carter (17), is shown in Figure 36. A maximum resistivity of about 20 microhm-cm at 20°C occurs at about 20% rhodium. The temperature coefficient of electrical resistivity, also determined by these investigators, has a rather flat minimum of about 0.0014 per °C (0-100°C) between 20 and 40% rhodium. Roeser and Wensel's (191) data for the resistivity at 0°C and the relative resistivity of platinum and the 10 and 13% rhodium platinum alloys for temperatures up to 1500°C are given in Table 39. Presumably these data are for high purity thermoelement grade metal.

TABLE 39
Resistivity and Relative Resistivity of Platinum and Rhodium-Platinum Alloys

	Platinum	10% Rhodium Platinum	13% Rhodium Platinum
Resistivity at 0 ° C. microhm-cm	9.83	18.4	19.0
Temperature ° C.	R_t/R_o		
0	1.000	1.000	1.000
100	1.392	1.166	1.156
200	1.773	1.330	1.308
300	2.142	1.490	1.456
400	2.499	1.646	1.601
500	2.844	1.798	1.744
600	3.178	1.947	1.885
700	3.500	2.093	2.023
800	3.810	2.234	2.157
900	4.109	2.370	2.287
1000	4.396	2.503	2.414
1100	4.671	2.633	2.538
1200	4.935	2.761	2.660
1300	5.187	2.887	2.780
1400	5.427	3.011	2.898
1500	5.655	3.133	3.014

THERMOELECTRIC PROPERTIES

The scientific and commercial importance of the rhodium platinum vs. platinum thermocouple has led to extensive investigation of the thermoelectric properties of this system of alloys by Sosman (92), Day and Sosman (93), Adams (94), Roeser and Wensel (95), Caldwell (96), Nemilow and Voronow (77) and others. The 10% rhodium platinum vs. pure platinum thermocouple, which is most frequently used, serves to define the International Temperature Scale between 660 and 1063°C. The corresponding temperature – emf values for this couple published by Adams in 1914, were based upon the gas thermometer determinations of Day and Sosman. After the adoption of the International Temperature Scale and the determination of some fixed points on this scale, the values given by Adams were slightly revised by Roeser and Wensel in 1933. Table 40 lists the emf of the 10% rhodium platinum vs. platinum thermocouple for temperatures up to 1720°C at intervals of 10°C as derived from Roeser and Wensel (95). Their original paper gives complete reference tables for the 10 and 13% rhodium platinum vs. platinum thermocouples.

TABLE 40
Thermal EMF of 10% Rhodium-Platinum vs. Platinum

Temp. ° C.	0	10	20	30	40	50	60	70	80	90
	MILLIVOLTS									
0	0	.057	.114	.174	.235	.299	.365	.432	.500	.571
100	.643	.717	.792	.869	.946	1.025	1.105	1.186	1.269	1.352
200	1.436	1.521	1.606	1.692	1.779	1.867	1.956	2.045	2.134	2.225
300	2.316	2.406	2.498	2.591	2.684	2.778	2.871	2.965	3.060	3.155
400	3.251	3.346	3.441	3.538	3.634	3.731	3.828	3.925	4.023	4.121
500	4.219	4.318	4.417	4.516	4.616	4.716	4.817	4.918	5.019	5.120
600	5.222	5.325	5.427	5.530	5.633	5.737	5.841	5.945	6.050	6.155
700	6.260	6.365	6.471	6.578	6.684	6.790	6.898	7.005	7.113	7.222
800	7.330	7.439	7.548	7.658	7.768	7.878	7.989	8.100	8.211	8.322
900	8.434	8.546	8.658	8.771	8.884	8.998	9.111	9.225	9.340	9.454
1000	9.569	9.685	9.800	9.916	10.033	10.149	10.266	10.383	10.500	10.618
1100	10.736	10.854	10.973	11.091	11.209	11.329	11.448	11.567	11.686	11.805
1200	11.924	12.043	12.163	12.283	12.402	12.522	12.642	12.762	12.881	13.000
1300	13.120	13.239	13.358	13.478	13.598	13.717	13.836	13.955	14.074	14.193
1400	14.312	14.431	14.550	14.668	14.787	14.906	15.024	15.143	15.261	15.379
1500	15.498	15.615	15.733	15.852	15.969	16.087	16.205	16.322	16.440	16.557
1600	16.674	16.792	16.908	17.026	17.142	17.259	17.376	17.492	17.608	17.724
1700	17.841	17.957	18.073	....	....	....	....	....	....	....

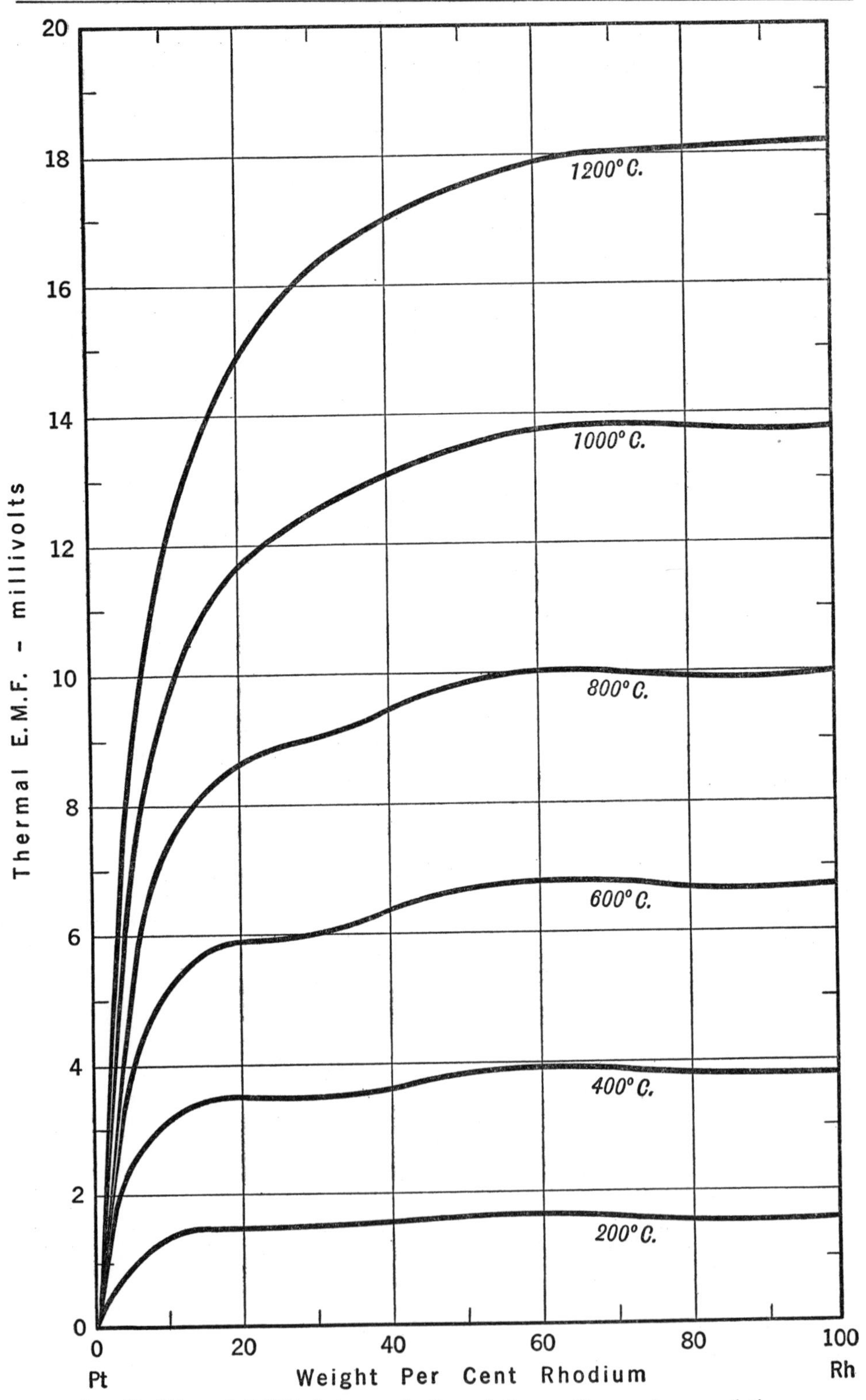

FIG. 37. *Thermal E.M.F. between rhodium-platinum alloys and pure platinum.*

The temperature—emf values for the series of alloys including pure rhodium, based upon the work of both Sosman and Caldwell are shown graphically in Figure 37. A change in slope of the curves between 20 and 40% rhodium at temperatures below 800°C and maxima at about 60% rhodium at temperatures below 1000°C are evident and may be indicative of solid transformations.

MECHANICAL PROPERTIES

Figure 38 shows the Brinell hardness of annealed alloys and is based upon the work of Acken (72), Nemilow and Voronow (77) and Carter (17). In the annealed condition, the hardness increases from about 40 BHN for platinum to about 90 BHN at about 50% rhodium and then remains almost constant to 100% rhodium. The Brinell hardness of the hard worked alloys increases from about 100 BHN for platinum to about 320 BHN for the 50% rhodium alloy according to Carter (17).

Wise and Eash's (27) values for the

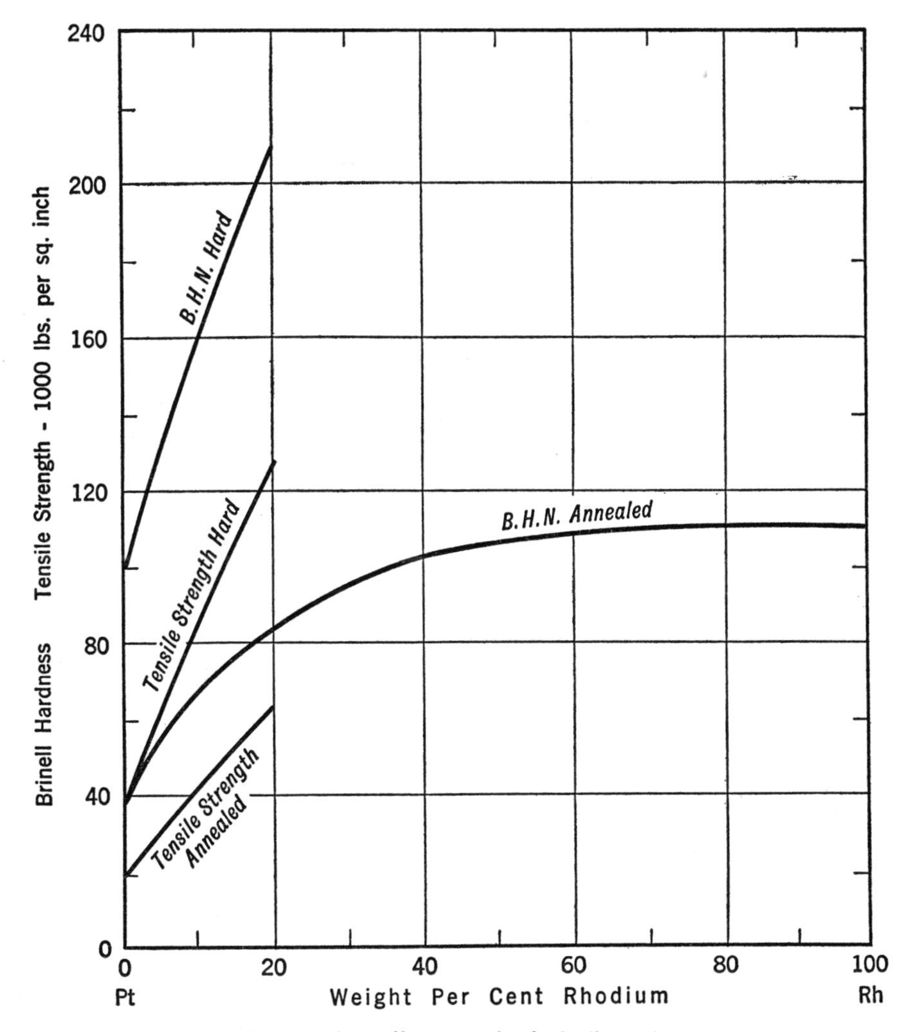

FIG. 38. *Hardness and tensile strength of rhodium-platinum alloys.*

ultimate tensile strength of the cold worked and annealed alloys containing up to 10% rhodium are shown in the same figure. They report an ultimate tensile strength of 84,000 lbs. per sq. in. for the cold worked (50% reduction) alloy and 38,500 lbs. per sq. in. after annealing at 1200°C. The mechanical properties of the platinum rich alloys containing up to 40% rhodium, taken from Carter and Stauss (172), are listed in Table 41.

TABLE 41
Properties of Platinum-Rhodium Alloys

% Rh	Brinell Hardness		Ultimate Tensile Strength Lbs. per sq. in.	
	Hard	Annealed	Hard	Annealed
0	97	42	34,000	18,000
3.5	120	60	60,000	25,000
5	130	70	70,000	30,000
10	165	90	90,000	45,000
20	210	120	130,000	70,000
40	290	150	....	....

Because the 10% rhodium platinum alloy is frequently used at high temperatures, such as in glass working equipment, furnace windings, thermocouples and ammonia oxidation catalysts, Table 42, taken from Carter and Stauss (172), is included to show the effect of temperature on the electrical resistivity and tensile strength of this alloy. The tensile values obtained by Wise and Eash (28) on the .050" diameter wires are also shown.

TABLE 42
Resistivity and Tensile Strength of 10% Rhodium 90% Platinum Alloy at Elevated Temperatures

Temperature ° C.	Resistivity		Ratio of Tensile Strength at Temperature to that at 20 ° C.		Tensile Strength lbs./sq. in.
			Wire Diameter		
	ohms/mil. ft.	microhm-cm	0.050"	0.010" and 0.003"	0.050"
20	114	19	1.0	1.0	48,000
500	203	33.7	0.66	0.71	32,000
700	236	39.3	0.54	0.57	26,000
900	267	44.4	0.38	0.43	18,000
1100	296	49.2	0.23	0.29	10,700
1300	324	53.9	......	0.15	......
1500	350	58.2	......	0.08	......

WORKABILITY

Alloys containing less than about 20% rhodium may be worked hot or cold while those containing between 20 and 40% rhodium must be hot worked prior to cold working. Other alloys are somewhat difficult to work and the practical limit of workability is about 40% rhodium.

CORROSION AND TARNISH RESISTANCE

The corrosion and tarnish resistance of the entire series of alloys is excellent, but in general the high rhodium alloys have a higher resistance to corrosion. Alloys with more than about 5% rhodium are slowly oxidized in air at temperatures between 750 and 1150°C with the formation of a superficial blue-black film, but at higher temperatures the oxide decomposes and the surface again becomes bright.

USES

Alloys with about 3.5% rhodium are used for crucibles as an alternative to pure platinum while alloys containing 10% rhodium are especially resistant to molten glass and are used for nozzles (sometimes electrically heated) in glass working equipment. Alloys with more than about 20% rhodium are unattacked by aqua regia and have uses similar to the 10% iridium platinum alloys in electrolytic processes. The 10% rhodium alloy has marked catalytic activity and is the standard catalyst for the oxidation of ammonia in the production of nitric acid although recently considerable use has been made of the 5% rhodium platinum alloy for this purpose. The 10% rhodium platinum alloy with carefully maintained composition serves as the positive element in the generally used platinum vs. rhodium platinum thermocouple, although some use is made of the 13% rhodium platinum vs. platinum thermocouple to comply with the emf temperature scales of certain pyrometers. Some use has also been made of thermocouples employing rhodium platinum alloys of different rhodium content for both thermocouple elements—one such combination is 15% rhodium platinum paired with 5% rhodium platinum. These couples have some advantage in ruggedness and can be used at slightly higher temperatures than those employing pure platinum for one element but they have a lower emf. Long life high temperature furnaces are wound with rhodium platinum alloys containing from 10 to 20% rhodium, or sometimes more rhodium. Recent tests have shown that the 10% rhodium platinum alloy gives better service than the 70% gold 30% platinum alloy in spinnerets for rayon production and its use for this purpose is growing. Rhodium platinum and rhodium iridium platinum alloys have been used for electrical contacts and both the rhodium platinum and iridium platinum alloys are employed, particularly in England, for electrodes in aircraft spark plugs.

RUTHENIUM PLATINUM

Ageew and Kusnezov (97) concluded from the results of an X-ray study of the platinum ruthenium alloys that, at least up to 55% ruthenium, the system comprises a continuous series of solid solutions.

Similarly Nemilow and Rudnizky (98) concluded from a study of the hardness and temperature coefficient of electrical resistance that the metals form a continuous series of solid solutions up to 68% ruthenium, the highest ruthenium content alloy studied. However, the high hardness and low ductility of the alloys containing more than about 10% ruthenium and the fact that the metals belong to different crystallographic systems may be cited against the existence of a continuous series of solid solutions at low temperatures.

ELECTRICAL PROPERTIES

Carter and Stauss (172) report the electrical resistivity of the 5 and 10% ruthenium alloys as 31.5 and 43 microhm-cm at 20°C respectively. For the temperature coefficient of electrical resistance over the range 25-100°C they give 0.00085 per °C for the 5% ruthenium alloy and 0.00083 per °C for the 10% ruthenium alloy.

MECHANICAL PROPERTIES

The mechanical properties of the alloys containing up to 10% ruthenium, mainly from Carter and Stauss (172), are given in Table 43.

TABLE 43
Mechanical Properties of Platinum-Ruthenium Alloys

% Ruthenium	Brinell Hardness		Ultimate Tensile Strength Lbs. per sq. in.	
	Hard	Annealed	Hard	Annealed
0	97	42	34,000	18,000
3	...	...	80,000	42,000
5	210	130	115,000	60,000
10	280	190	150,000	85,000

CORROSION AND TARNISH RESISTANCE

The addition of ruthenium to platinum rapidly increases the resistance to aqua regia and nascent chlorine, the resistance being roughly equivalent to that of platinum iridium alloys with comparable iridium content. For all the platinum-rich alloys the tarnish resistance is, of course, extremely high. When heated in air, ruthenium is selectively oxidized from ruthenium platinum alloys, although less vigorously than osmium and at temperatures above 900°C ruthenium alloys lose weight due to the volatilization of the oxide.

WORKABILITY

The practical limit of workability is about 15% ruthenium, according to Carter (51), although the 13% alloy is quite workable under proper conditions. Ruthenium alloys should preferably be annealed under non-oxidizing conditions to prevent the formation and volatilization of ruthenium oxide.

USES

Ruthenium platinum alloys are used for contacts in high tension magnetos, the 10% alloy being most popular. Alloys containing lower percentages of ruthenium are also used for jewelry purposes. For this latter use the 5% ruthenium alloy has properties of the same order as the 10% iridium platinum alloy which has been so popular in the United States. More complex alloys are used for tipping pen nibs.

SILICON PLATINUM

Three eutectics are formed in the platinum silicon system according to Voronow (133). The first, between platinum and Pt_5Si_{12} contains about 4.4% silicon and melts at about 825°C. Between Pt_2Si and PtSi, the second eutectic, which contains about 8.2% silicon and melts at about 980°C, is formed. A third eutectic containing about 22% silicon exists between PtSi and silicon and melts at about 980°C. Of the three compounds. Pt_5Si_{12} (5.4% silicon) is formed by a peritectic reaction at 980°C while Pt_2Si (6.7% silicon) and PtSi (12.6% silicon) melt at 1090° and 1230°C respectively. The compound Pt_2Si undergoes a transformation at about 700°C but the nature of this change has not been determined. Voronow gives the solid solubility of silicon in platinum as about 0.2% at the solidus temperature, but this may be somewhat high.

MECHANICAL PROPERTIES

Voronow (133) studied the effect of silicon additions to platinum on the hardness of quenched alloys. He reported that the Brinell hardness increased from 25.2 BHN for platinum to 132 BHN at 0.10% silicon, decreased to 27.6 BHN at 0.20% silicon and then increased to 268 BHN at 5.10% silicon. The reason for the curious result is not evident. Platinum containing sufficient silicon to form the low melting eutectic phase is brittle.

SILVER PLATINUM

Doerinckel (99) determined the liquidus and solidus of platinum silver alloys containing 20 to 90% silver. Thompson and Miller (169) investigated the silver-rich alloys and found that those containing more than about 70% silver were single phase while those containing less than 70% were duplex.

Later, Kurnakow and Nemilow (104) investigated the system by means of hardness and electrical conductivity

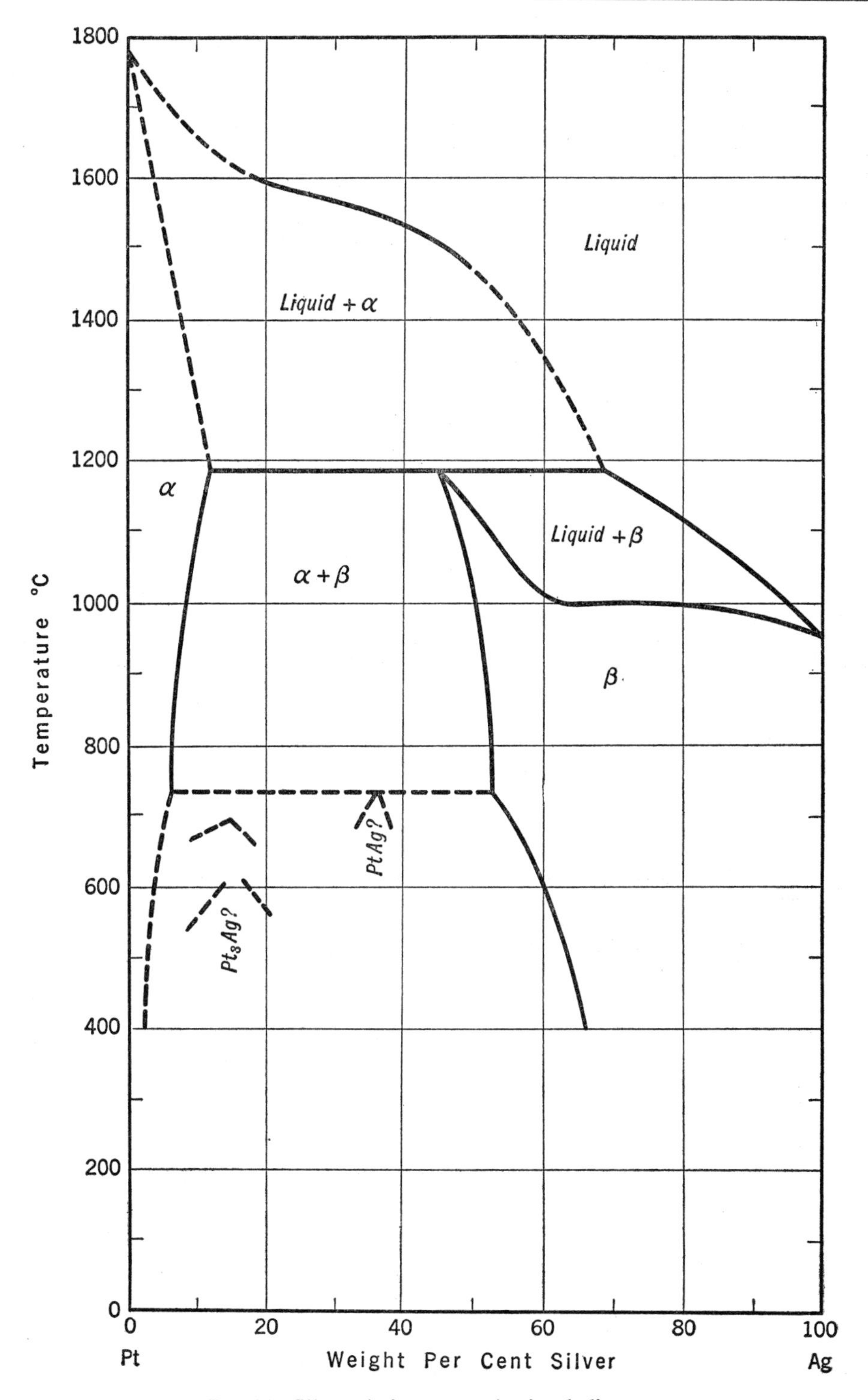

FIG. 39. *Silver-platinum constitutional diagram.*

measurements and concluded that between about 13 and 60% silver two solid solutions exist. Johansson and Linde (105), by resistance measurements and determinations of the lattice structure, brought the diagram to its present state which is shown in **Figure 39.**

It is now believed that the platinum silver system consists of two series of solid solutions which co-exist over the range 12 to 45% silver at the solidus temperature. The duplex range widens at lower temperatures and at 400°C extends from about 2 to 66% silver. Johansson and Linde (105) suggest further low temperature transformations based upon Pt_3Ag (15.55% silver) and PtAg (35.59% silver) and involving ordering. The marked precipitation hardening observed by Wise and Vines (173) in the 15 to 35% silver alloys offers some support to this suggestion. The exact boundaries of these phase regions, resulting from the interaction of the two saturated solid solutions, have not been established, as the phenomena accompanying them are very complicated and difficultly reproducible.

ELECTRICAL RESISTIVITY

The resistivity of the single phase alloys, according to Johansson and Linde (105) and Kurnakow and Nemilow (104) is given in **Figure 40.** A maximum of about 61 microhm-cm at 45% silver is evident. For the duplex alloys the resistivity varies with the thermal treatment and is lower than that of the single phase alloys of the same composition. The temperature coefficient of electrical resistance for the platinum-rich and silver-rich alloys is also shown in the same figure. Kurna-

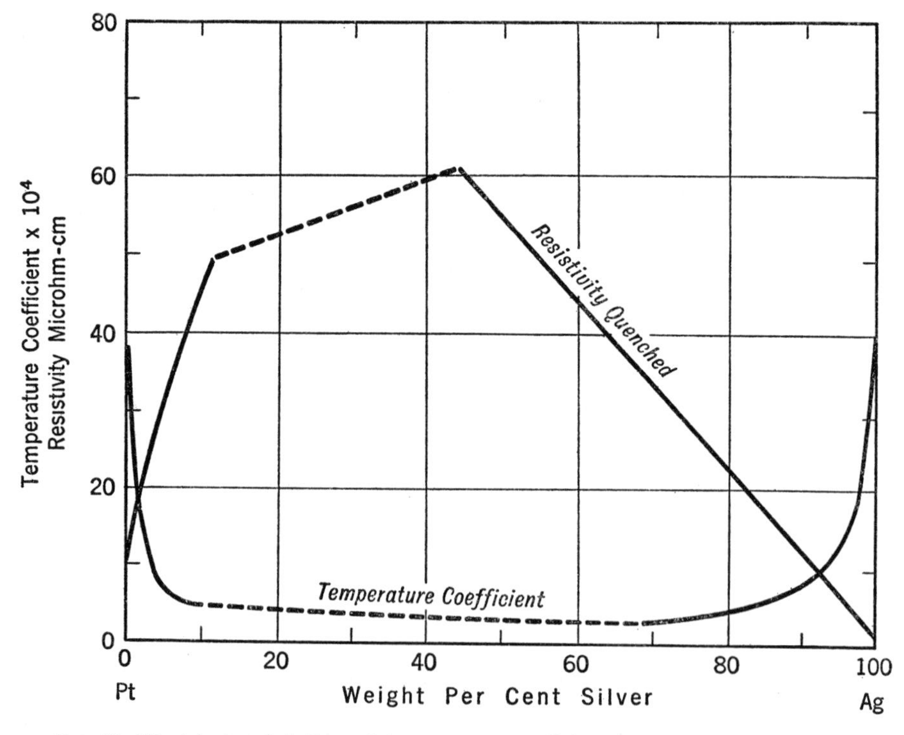

FIG. 40. *Electrical resistivity and temperature coefficient of silver-platinum alloys.*

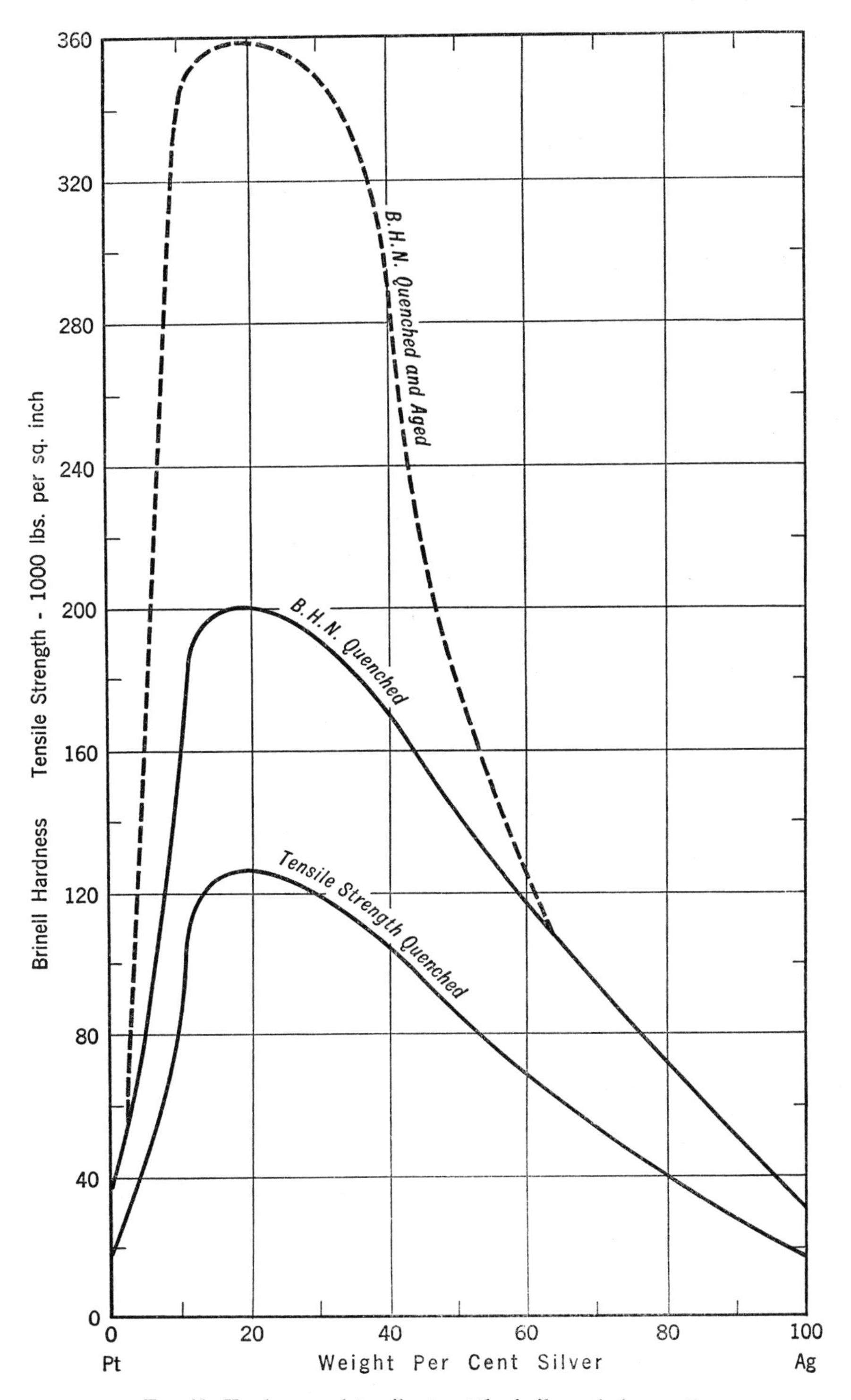

FIG. 41. *Hardness and tensile strength of silver-platinum alloys.*

kow and Nemilow report a minimum coefficient of 0.00022 per °C (25-100°C) at 69% silver.

MECHANICAL PROPERTIES

The Brinell hardness values of alloys quenched from 950 to 1050°C, depending upon the silver content, are shown in Figure 41. According to Kurnakow and Nemilow, a maximum hardness of about 200 BHN occurs at 20% silver, in the annealed condition. Marked precipitation hardening occurs in the range 10 to 40% silver and hardnesses as high as 360 BHN may be obtained by aging quenched alloys at about 550°C (173).

The tensile strength of alloys quenched from 800°C, based upon the work of Carter (17) and Kurnakow and Nemilow (104), is shown in the same figure. A maximum tensile strength of about 127,000 lbs. per sq. in. occurs at about 20% silver.

WORKABILITY

Due to the persistence of the cored structure developed on solidification and complicated phase changes, alloys containing less than about 75% silver are somewhat difficult to work. However, proper annealing above 800°C followed by quenching and working increases the ductility so that with care the entire series may be wrought.

CORROSION AND TARNISH RESISTANCE

The corrosion and tarnish resistance of the alloys decreases with increase in silver content and from the nature of the system, it is believed that the duplex alloys will be no more noble than the silver-rich solid solution contained in them. Alloys containing more than about 60% silver are rapidly attacked by nitric acid and ferric chloride and tarnished by exposure to industrial atmospheres.

COLOR

All alloys are white in color, although they are less brilliant than the pure end members.

USES

Silver-rich alloys containing a few percent of platinum are used for electrical contacts. Ternary alloys containing sufficient palladium to make them resistant to tarnishing are employed in the dental field for high strength wires.

SULPHUR PLATINUM

The system platinum sulphur has not been adequately investigated but it is known that a relatively unstable compound PtS exists. Jedele (131) determined the tensile strength and elongation at room temperature and at 850°C of platinum containing fractional percentages of sulphur. His results show that the presence of 0.02% sulphur in platinum has little effect on the ductility at room temperature or at 850°C. The presence of 0.06% sulphur in platinum markedly reduced the elongation although Jedele states that this alloy worked as easily as pure platinum. The alloy with 0.23% sulphur was, however, difficult to work.

Platinum shows extraordinary resistance to sulphurous atmospheres at high temperature. At temperatures up to 1100°C sulphur dioxide has no more effect on platinum than air. In hydrogen sulphide platinum is very slightly attacked with the formation of a thin blue film. However, the film appears to be protective and there is no evidence of intergranular penetration or embrittlement. The blue film formed on exposing platinum to hot hydrogen sulphide is readily decomposed in air at temperatures above about 600°C.

MECHANICAL PROPERTIES

The mechanical properties of platinum containing small amounts of sulphur, after Jedele (131), are given in Table 44.

TABLE 44
Mechanical Properties of Platinum-Sulphur Alloys at Room Temperature and 850°C

	Room Temperature			850 °C.	
Sulphur %	Brinell Hardness	Tensile Strength Lbs. per sq. in.	Elongation %	Tensile Strength Lbs. per sq. in.	Elongation %
0.23	93	......	...	......	...
0.15	60	28,200	14.7	12,300	5.8
0.06	50	23,600	10.1	9,800	5.5
0.02	45	23,000	26.2	10,500	14.0
0.005	45	21,700	24.7	7,500	14.5
0.000	45	21,000	27.1	9,800	9.0

TUNGSTEN PLATINUM

Muller (120) found that the liquidus of this system increases rapidly from the melting point of platinum to about 2350°C at 50% tungsten and suggested that a continuous series of solid solutions formed throughout this range. However, Kremer (121) observed that although the 8% tungsten alloy was a solid solution, the 26% tungsten alloy contained an eutectic or intermediate phase. Further investigation is required to clear up this matter and to determine the nature of the system at higher tungsten contents, and its response to age hardening treatments.

ELECTRICAL PROPERTIES

Rhodes (200) determined the electrical resistivity of platinum tungsten alloys containing up to 6% tungsten. His values for the electrical resistivities at 20°C are 21.5, 36 and 50 microhm-cm respectively for the 2, 4 and 6% tungsten alloys.

MECHANICAL PROPERTIES

Rhodes (200) also determined the mechanical properties of these alloys containing up to 7% tungsten with results as shown in Figure 42. These data were obtained on wire cold drawn 50% reduction in area, and sheet cold rolled 50% reduction in thickness, tested as cold worked, and after annealing at 1200°C for 5 minutes. It is evident from these data that tungsten is a very effective hardener for platinum.

USES

The most promising fields for these alloys and their derivatives are for electrical contacts, for hard corrosion resisting instrument bearings, and pen tipping materials.

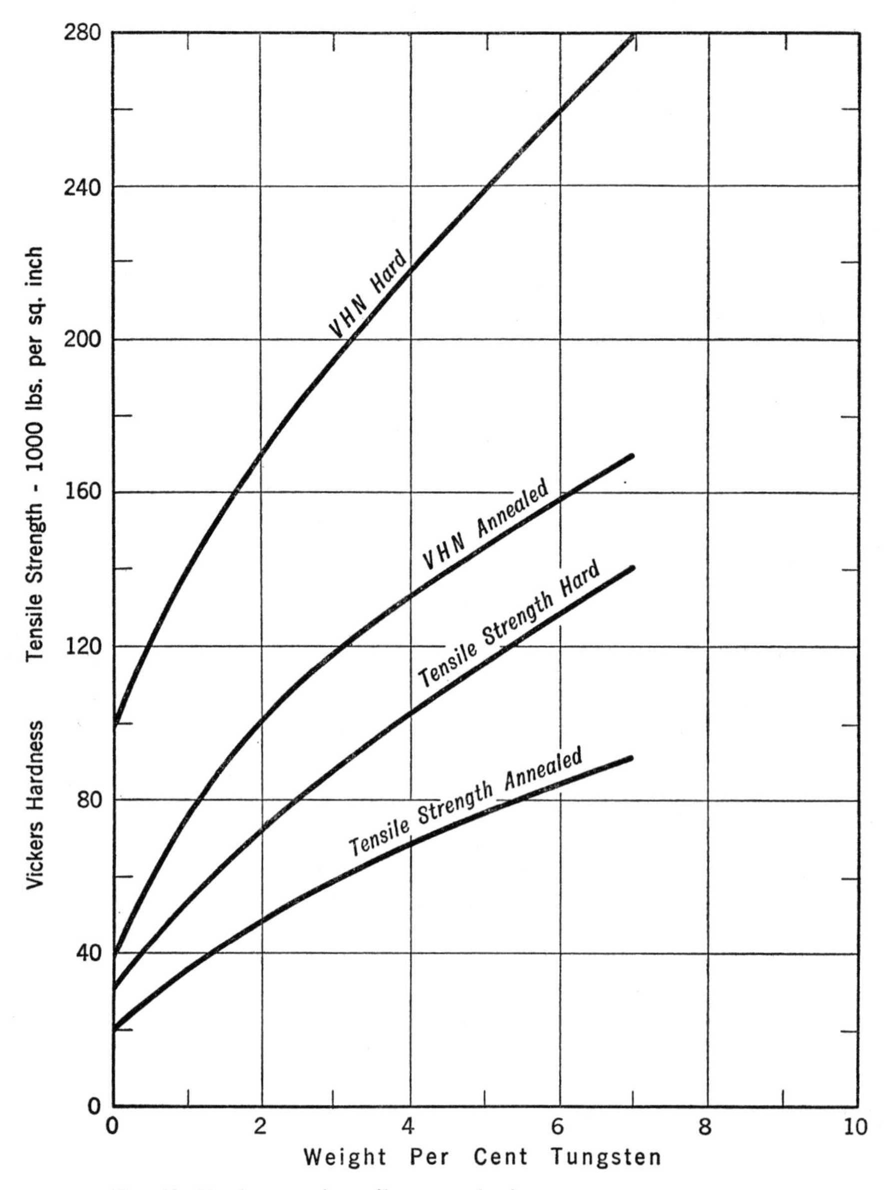

FIG. 42. *Hardness and tensile strength of tungsten-platinum alloys.*

PALLADIUM ALLOYS

ANTIMONY PALLADIUM

The palladium antimony system, which is somewhat similar to the palladium lead system, has been studied by Sander (166) and Grigoriev (165). The palladium-rich portion comprises a solid solution, a compound Pd_3Sb (27% antimony) and an eutectic between these two phases. The solid solubility of antimony in palladium has not been determined but is believed to be in the neighborhood of 15% at the solidus temperature. Grigoriev gives 1065°C and 23% antimony for the eutectic point, while Sander found 1070°C and 23.5%. The compound Pd_3Sb (27% antimony) melts at about 1200°C and undergoes a transformation in the solid state at about 950°C. At higher antimony contents two other eutectics containing about 45 and 90% antimony and melting at about 730 and 595°C respectively, and two compounds PdSb and $PdSb_2$, are formed.

MECHANICAL PROPERTIES

The 15% antimony alloy has a Vickers hardness of 132 when annealed at 800°C, and 272 when cold rolled 50% reduction from the casting. This alloy had a small amount of a second phase present around the grain boundaries after quenching from 800°C and in this condition it was not ductile.

BERYLLIUM PALLADIUM

Winkler (202) studied the palladium rich end of the palladium beryllium system by thermal analysis and metallographic examination. An eutectic, at 930°C and 2.07% Be, is formed between palladium and the compound Pd Be (7.8%Be) which melts at 1460°C. Four other compounds are formed by peritectic reactions; Pd_3Be (2.7% Be) at 960°C, Pd_2Be (4.05% Be) at 1090°C, Pd_3Be_2 (5.34% Be) at 1170°C and Pd_4Be_3 (6% Be) at 1200°C. A reaction in the solid state at 1055°C in the neighborhood of 7.8% Be is also evident.

BORON PALLADIUM

According to Sieverts and Bruning (203), a cast palladium boron alloy containing 0.75% boron consisted of a single phase after holding for 44 hours at 700°C while other alloys containing 1.6% boron and 2% boron were duplex. Pearson's (211) work shows that a low melting eutectic is formed in the palladium boron system. In melting palladium-rich alloys care must be taken to avoid excessive contamination with boron which may be reduced from fluxes and produce hot shortness. However, minute amounts of boron, generally added as calcium boride, are frequently added to palladium alloys to deoxidize them.

CARBON PALLADIUM

This system has not been investigated in detail but it is known that palladium, like platinum, readily dissolves carbon when molten and rejects it as graphite on solidification. It is believed that an eutectic which melts only slightly lower than palladium is formed and that the solid solubility of carbon in palladium is very low. According to Siebert (185) palladium carbon melts containing up to 5% of carbon are tough. The hardness of these alloys is, however, not very high.

CHROMIUM PALLADIUM

The palladium chromium system comprises a solid solution between palladium and the compound Pd_2Cr_3, a chromium-rich solid solution and an eutectic between these two phases, according to Grube and Knabe (160). The liquidus and solidus of the palladium-rich solid solution lie close together decreasing from the melting point of palladium to a minimum of 1300°C at 38% chromium and then increasing sharply to a maximum of 1398°C at the compound Pd_2Cr_3 (42% chromium) as shown in Figure 43. An

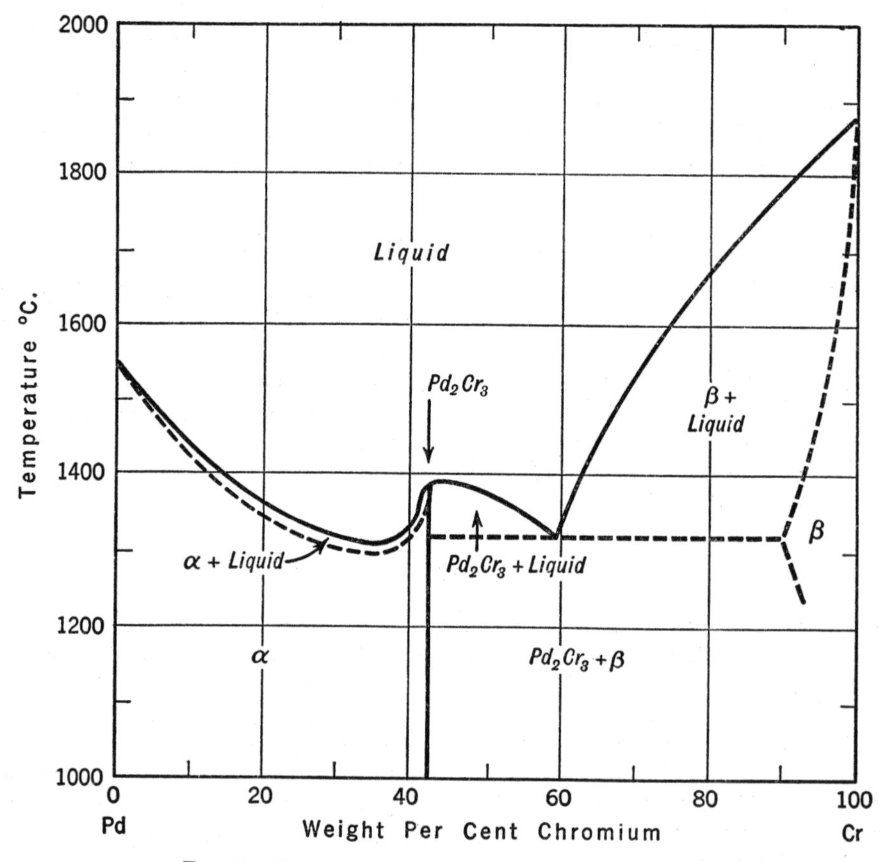

FIG. 43. *Chromium-palladium constitutional diagram.*

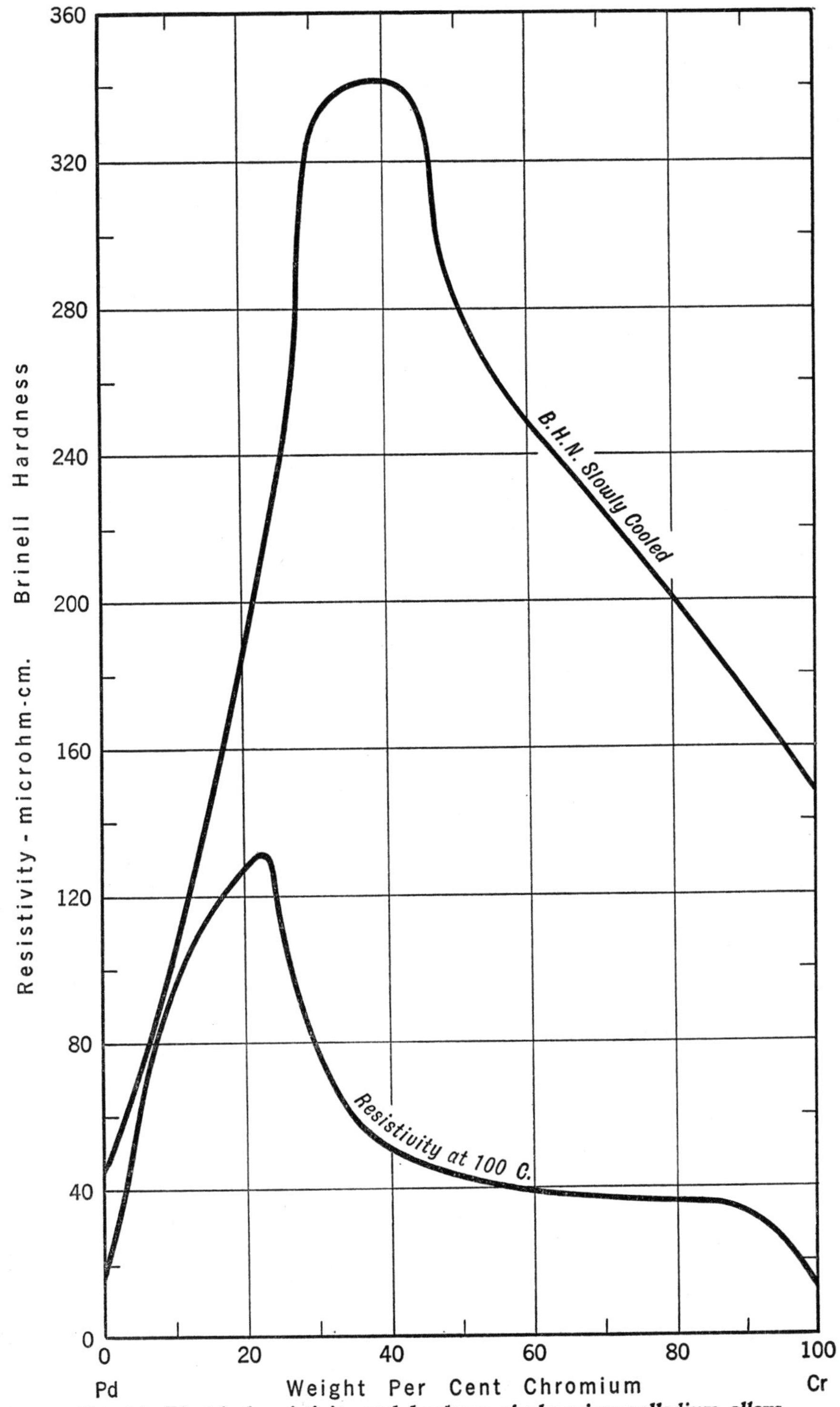

FIG. 44. *Electrical resistivity and hardness of chromium-palladium alloys.*

eutectic horizontal, between Pd_2Cr_3 and the chromium-rich solid solution, extends from 42 to 90.5% chromium at 1320°C the eutectic composition being 59.5% chromium. At the solidus temperature, the chromium-rich solid solution dissolves up to about 10% palladium. Low temperature solubilities and possible transformations have not been adequately investigated.

ELECTRICAL PROPERTIES

The addition of chromium to palladium rapidly increases the electrical resistivity. According to Grube and Knabe (160), the electrical resistivity, at 100°C, reaches a sharp maximum of 133 microhm-cm at 23% chromium in slowly cooled alloys as shown in Figure 44. They also determined the electrical resistivity for the entire series of alloys at temperatures up to 1300°C. Carter (51) reports the electrical resistivity of the 2.5 and 5.0% chromium alloys as 24.7 and 41 microhm-cm respectively.

MECHANICAL PROPERTIES

A maximum hardness of about 340 BHN occurs at about 40% chromium in slowly cooled alloys according to Grube and Knabe (160). Carter (51) gives 32,100 lbs. per sq. in. and 75,900 lbs. per sq. in. respectively for the tensile strength of the annealed and hard 2.5% chromium alloy. His values for the tensile strengths of the annealed and hard 5% chromium alloys are 38,700 lbs. per sq. in. and 91,200 lbs. per sq. in. respectively.

USES

Alloys containing up to 25% Cr with or without additions of nickel or cobalt have properties which may render them useful for dental purposes and spark plug electrodes.

COBALT PALLADIUM

An unbroken series of solid solutions crystallize from palladium cobalt melts but since the liquidus and solidus have a minimum and cobalt suffers a transformation, low temperature transformations are to be expected. According to Grube and Kastner (156), the liquidus and solidus remain close together throughout, the minimum occurring at 1217°C and 35.5% (50 atomic percent) cobalt as shown in Figure 45. Grube and Winkler (157), investigating the system magnetically, found evidence of low temperature transformations in the high cobalt alloys but concluded that alloys containing up to about 75% cobalt were devoid of phase transformations in the solid state. The Curie temperature increases smoothly from 30°C for the 5.5% cobalt alloy to 1119°C for pure cobalt (157).

ELECTRICAL PROPERTIES

The electrical resistivity at 40°C reaches a maximum of 38 microhm-cm at about 12% (25 atomic percent) cobalt according to Grube and Kastner (156). At 800°C the maximum of about 100 microhm-cm occurs at about 36% (50 atomic percent) cobalt.

MECHANICAL PROPERTIES

The Vickers hardness of annealed palladium-rich alloys increases smoothly from 44 VHN for palladium to about 200 VHN for the 50% cobalt alloy.

WORKABILITY

The palladium-rich alloys are quite ductile and are easily worked.

CORROSION AND TARNISH RESISTANCE

The corrosion and tarnish resistance of these alloys is similar to that of the pal-

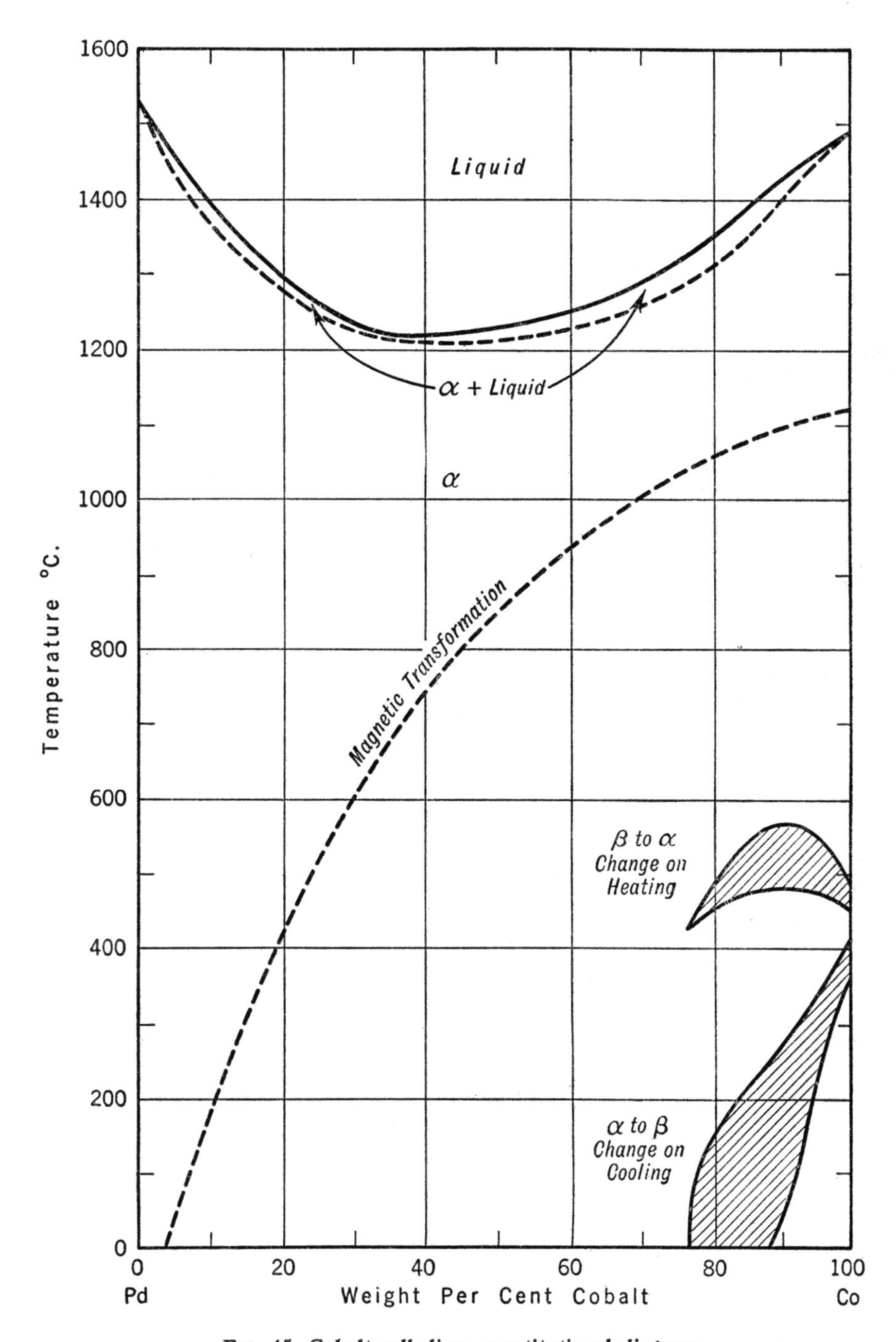

FIG. 45. *Cobalt-palladium constitutional diagram.*

ladium nickel alloys of comparable palladium content.

COLOR

All alloys are substantially white in color.

USES

The palladium cobalt alloys have been suggested for use as electrical contacts and for jewelry and dental purposes.

COPPER PALLADIUM

The system of palladium copper comprises a continuous series of face centered cubic solid solutions above about 600°C. According to Ruer (146), the liquidus and solidus remain close together and descend smoothly from the melting point of palladium to that of copper as shown in Figure 46. Ordering transformations, based on PdCu and $PdCu_3$, occur at low temperatures, but the transformation temperature maxima and electrical resistivity minima appear to be displaced from the simple atomic ratios PdCu and $PdCu_3$. The transformation based upon PdCu (37.4% copper) occurs over the range 31 to 60% copper; beginning at about 600°C and 46% copper according to Taylor (147) and Jones and Sykes (148). Johansson and Linde (149) previously proposed an unsymmetrical range terminating sharply at PdCu (37.4% copper) and, in explanation, suggested that the palladium atoms were unable to replace copper atoms in the body centered cubic lattice. The transformation in this range involves a change in lattice to an ordered body centered cubic structure of the caesium chloride type but this lattice change is only complete in the range 41 to 51% copper according to Jones and Sykes (148).

Another transformation based upon $PdCu_3$ (64% copper) develops in the range 61 to 87% copper, beginning at about 500°C according to Jones and Sykes (148). These investigators, who studied the system by means of X-ray diffraction measurements and reinterpreted Taylor's (147) results on resistance measurements, found that alloys containing between 61 and 72% copper transformed to an ordered tetragonal lattice, while those containing 72 to 87% copper became ordered but retained their face centered cubic lattice. The change in the axial ratio of the alloys to form the tetragonal lattice in the former range is slight as has been previously noted. Belogonov (151) indicates a further transformation in the $PdCu_3$ range which takes place at a constant temperature of about 300°C but this is not evident in the works of other researchers.

The transformations in both ranges, PdCu and $PdCu_3$, are accelerated by cold work and from the work of Reeve (181) it is believed that the one based on PdCu is also accelerated by hydrogen. Seemann (182) also found that cold work destroyed the ordered body centered cubic lattice of the PdCu range alloys converting it to the random face centered cubic lattice. The alloys show less age hardening than might be expected from the suggested transformations, but with the addition of moderate amounts of a third element, silver for example, marked age hardening can be secured as shown by Wise (201).

ELECTRICAL PROPERTIES

Electrical resistivity measurements by Johannson and Linde (149), Svensson (142), Stockdale (152) and Taylor (147) agree fairly well and place the

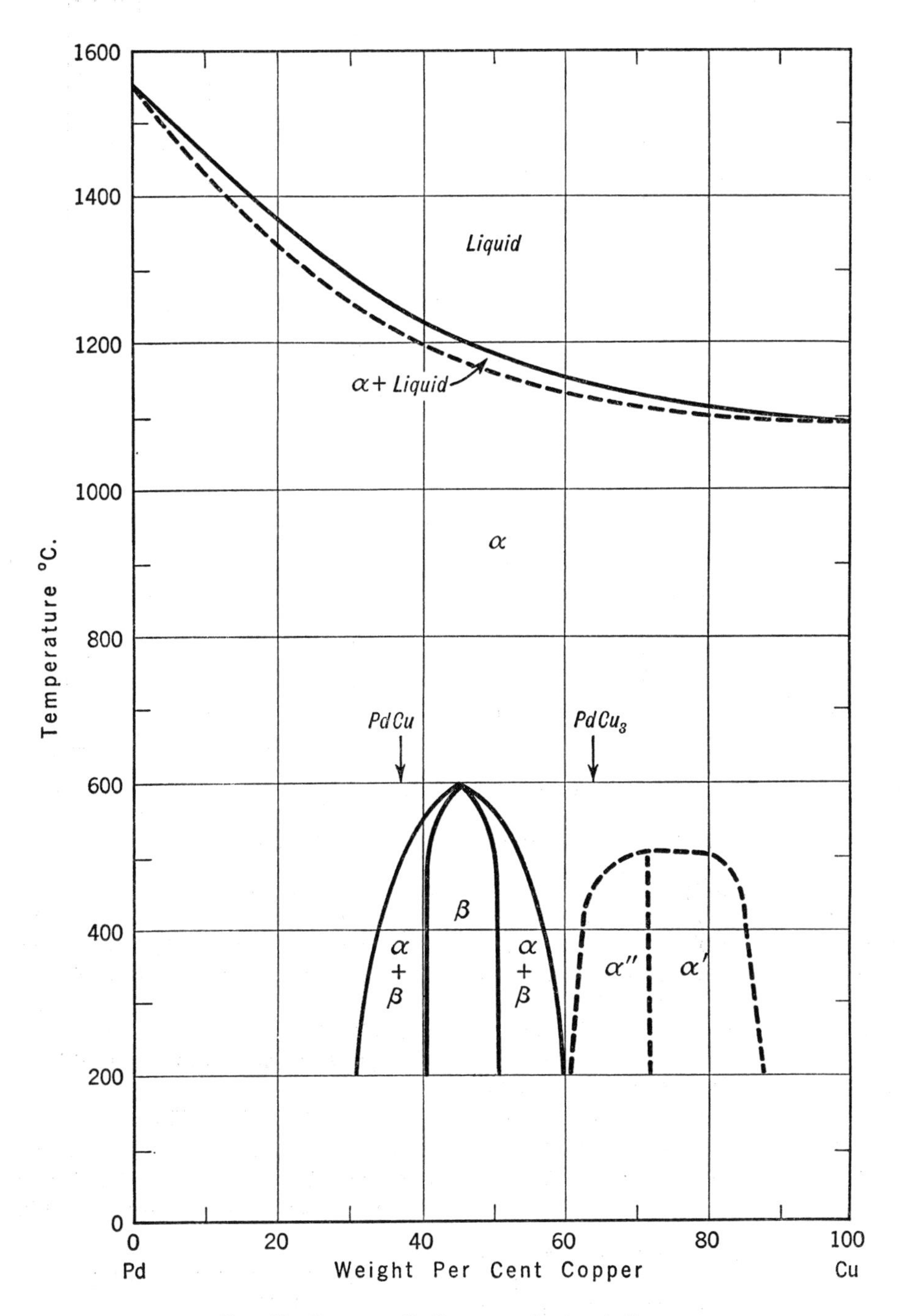

FIG. 46. ***Copper-palladium constitutional diagram.***

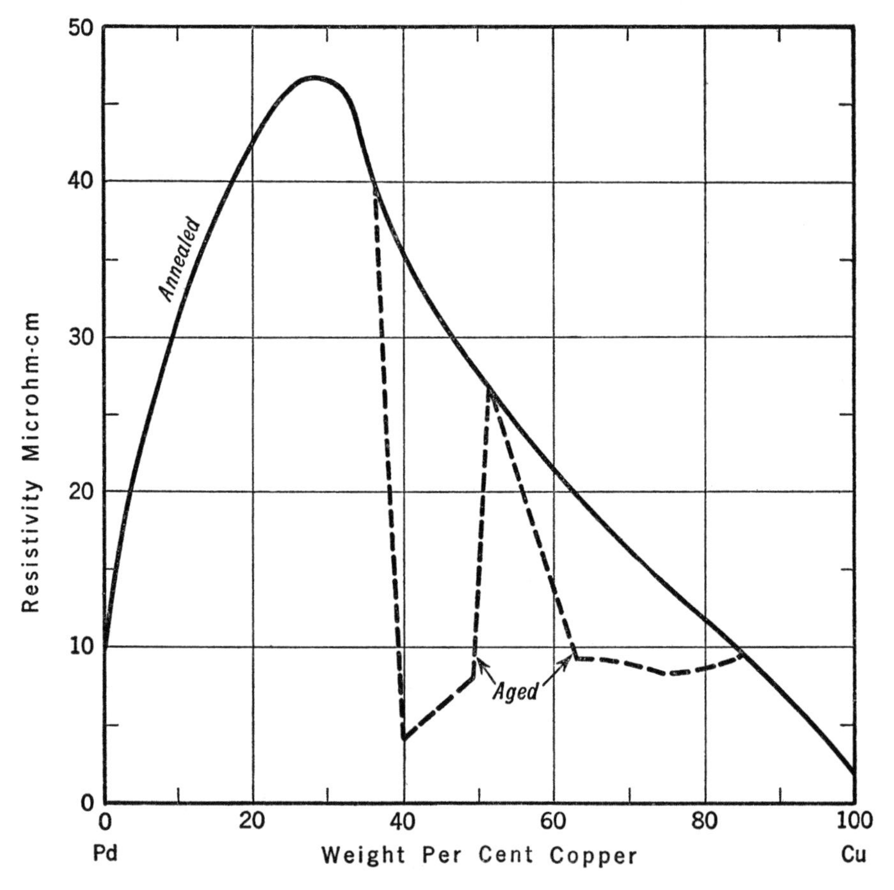

FIG. 47. *Electrical resistivity of copper-palladium alloys.*

maximum resistivity of 47 microhm-cm for the homogeneous unordered face centered cubic alloys at about 28% copper. Minimum resistivities in the ordered state of 4 and 8.1 microhm-cm occur at about 40 and 75% copper respectively, according to Svensson (142) as shown in Figure 47. Other investigators obtained somewhat lower minimum resistivities in the ordered state by the use of slower cooling rates.

MECHANICAL PROPERTIES

In the annealed condition a maximum hardness of about 120 BHN occurs at about 40% copper. For alloys cold rolled 66%, the maximum hardness of about 255 BHN also occurs at 40% copper. Only very slight hardening is obtained by aging for short times at temperatures below 600°C according to Wise and Vines (173) and Carter (51). The tensile strength reaches a maximum of about 92,000 lbs. per sq. in. at about 35% copper according to Wise (109) as shown in Figure 48.

WORKABILITY

The ductility of the face centered cubic unordered alloys is quite good and they can be readily worked with reasonable care.

CORROSION AND TARNISH RESISTANCE

The corrosion and tarnish resistance is intermediate between that of the two end members. Palladium copper alloys

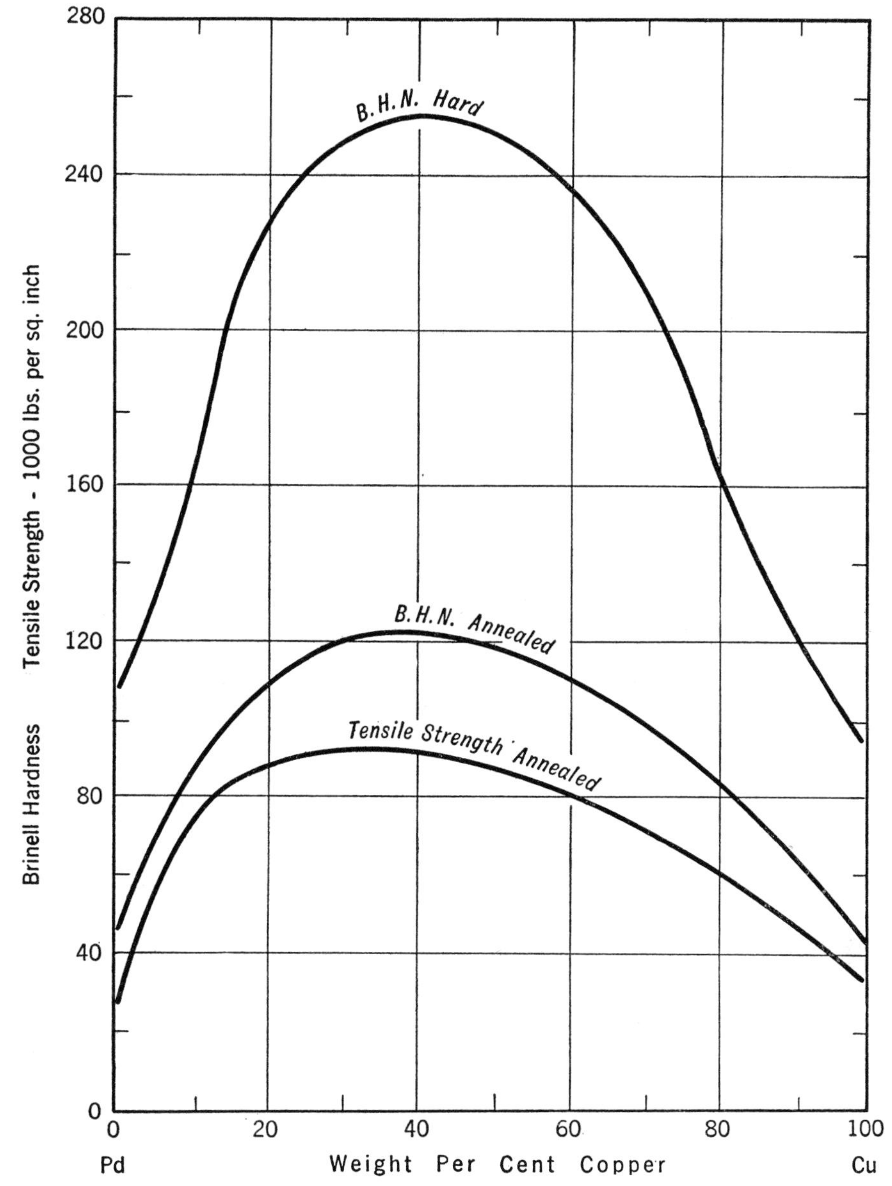

FIG. 48. *Hardness and tensile strength of copper-palladium alloys.*

tarnish more readily than palladium silver alloys with the same percentage of palladium.

COLOR

Alloys containing less than about 70% copper are white; higher copper content alloys ranging from white to the red color of copper.

USES

The 60% palladium alloy, sometimes after an ordering heat treatment, is used for electrical contacts, particularly in situations where appreciable electrostatic capacity is present in associated circuits, and is notable for its long life and smooth wear under these difficult operating conditions.

GOLD PALLADIUM

The system palladium gold appears to consist of a continuous series of solid solutions free from transformations in the solid state. The liquidus falls slowly with increasing gold content up to about 60% gold, and then drops more rapidly as the gold end of the series is approached. The solidus lies close to the liquidus throughout. Figure 49 shows Ruer's (135) diagram which was subsequently confirmed by Fraenkel and Stern (136). The electrical resistivity investigated by Geibel (137), Sedstrom (106), Schulze (88), Wise (109), Carter (17), and Rohl (138); the temperature coefficient of electrical resistivity determined by Geibel (137) and Carter (51), the thermal conductivity measured by Schulze (88) and Sedstrom (106); the linear coefficient of expansion determined by Johansson (139); the lattice measurements of Holgerson and Sedstrom (140) and Stenzel and Weerts (102) and the mechanical properties found by Wise (109) and Carter (17 and 51) all tend to confirm Ruer's conclusion that the system is devoid of transformations in the solid state. However, the peculiar change in slope of electrical property—composition curves in the neighborhood of 70% gold requires explanation.

ELECTRICAL PROPERTIES

Electrical resistivities obtained by Carter, Geibel, Schulze, Sedstrom and Wise agree very closely and place the maximum resistivity of about 27.5 microhm-cm at about 50% gold as shown in Figure 50. A minimum temperature coefficient of electrical resistivity of about 0.00034 per °C (0-100°C) occurs at about 60% gold. The peculiar change in slope in the electrical resistivity and

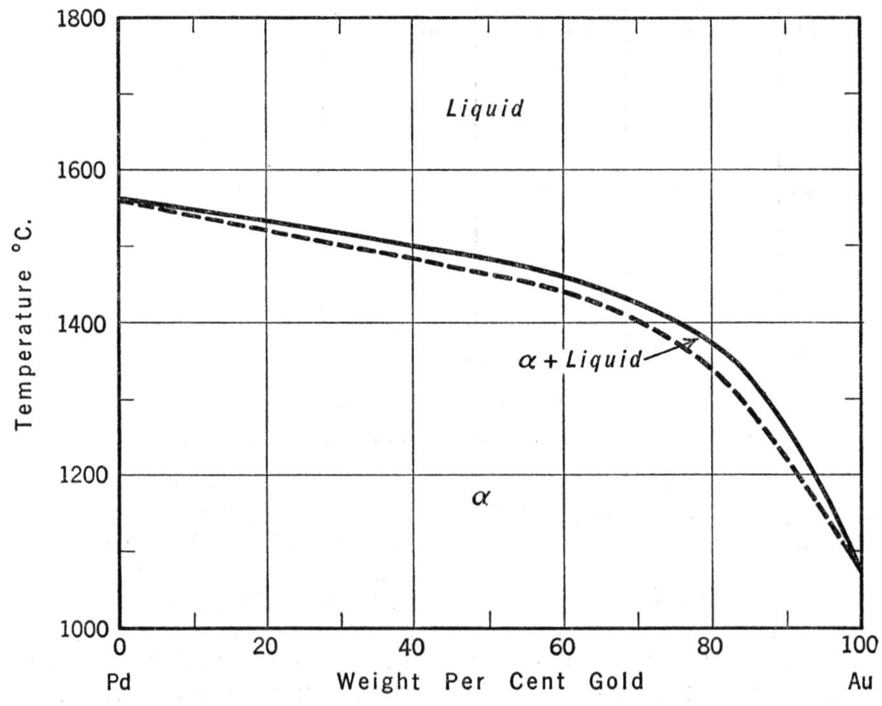

FIG. 49. *Gold-palladium constitutional diagram.*

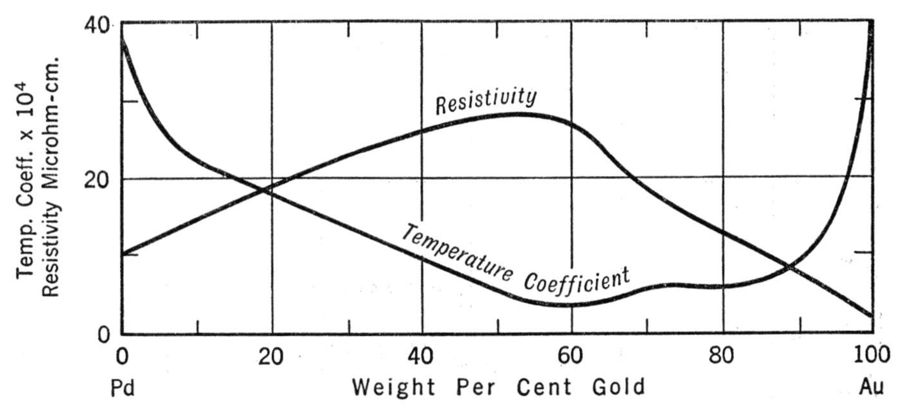

FIG. 50. *Electrical resistivity and temperature coefficient of gold-palladium alloys.*

temperature coefficient of electrical resistivity curves in the neighborhood of 70% gold has not been explained.

Thermal emf values of gold palladium alloys vs. platinum as obtained by Sivil (26) are given in Table 45. Isotherms of these values also show a change of slope in the neighborhood of 70% gold.

MECHANICAL PROPERTIES

Figure 51 gives the hardness values of the cold worked and the annealed alloys. These show maxima of about 160 BHN for the cold worked (66% reduction) alloys and 88 BHN for the annealed alloys in the neighborhood of 55% gold. The tensile strength curves, as determined by Wise (109), show rather flat maxima of 83,000 lbs. per sq. in. and 50,000 lbs. per sq. in. respectively for the cold drawn and annealed 55% gold alloys.

WORKABILITY

All the alloys are very ductile and are easily worked.

CORROSION AND TARNISH RESISTANCE

The corrosion and tarnish resistance of these alloys is very good. Alloys containing more than 10% gold are resistant to tarnish by industrial sulphur bearing atmospheres and those with more than 20% gold are resistant to nitric acid.

TABLE 45
Thermal EMF of Gold-Palladium Alloys vs. Platinum

Weight % Gold	0	10	20	30	40	50	60	70	80	90	100
Temp. ° C.	EMF Millivolts										
100	−0.7	−1.2	−1.4	−1.8	−2.3	−2.9	−3.7	−2.6	−0.5	+0.1	+1.0
200	−1.2	−2.3	−2.9	−3.2	−4.5	−5.8	−7.5	−5.3	−0.9	+0.2	+2.2
300	−1.7	−3.8	−4.6	−5.8	−7.0	−9.3	−11.0	−7.3	−1.4	+0.3	+3.2
400	−2.6	−4.7	−6.4	−8.0	−9.7	−13.2	−15.4	−11.0	−2.0	+0.5	+4.6
500	−3.7	−6.4	−8.5	−10.7	−13.0	−17.0	−20.0	−14.4	−2.8	+0.7	+6.3
600	−5.0	−8.0	−10.7	−13.6	−16.5	−21.2	−24.6	−17.3	−3.8	+1.0	+8.1
700	−6.3	−9.7	−13.0	−16.5	−20.4	−25.7	−29.3	−21.3	−4.9	+1.4	+10.1
800	−8.0	−11.7	−15.5	−19.8	−24.1	−30.2	−34.0	−24.9	−6.2	+1.7	+12.3
900	−9.5	−14.1	−18.2	−23.0	−27.9	−34.6	−38.5	−28.5	−7.5	+2.1	+14.7
1000	−11.5	−16.3	−20.8	−26.3	−31.7	−39.0	−43.0	−32.3	−9.1	+2.6	+17.0

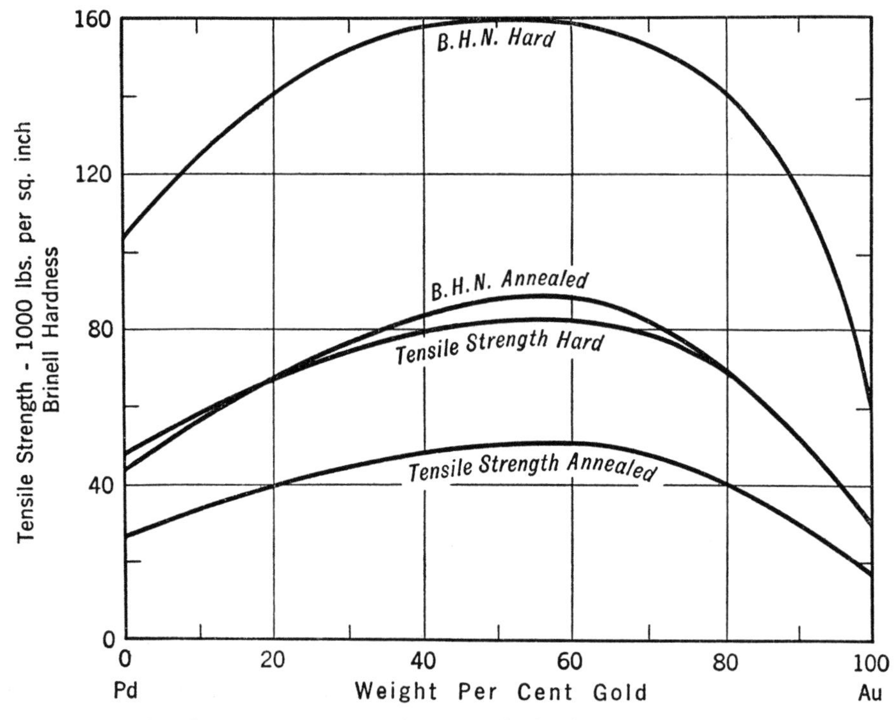

Fig. 51. *Hardness and tensile strength of gold-palladium alloys.*

COLOR

Palladium rapidly effaces the yellow color of gold so that alloys containing more than about 15% palladium are quite white.

USES

The high melting point and corrosion resistance of these alloys has at times led to their use as platinum substitutes for chemical ware. They have also been widely used for sleeves fired into porcelain teeth to which the supporting pins are attached, and modified alloys have been used for solid pins attached directly to the porcelain. Large quantities of palladium are used in complex palladium gold base alloys employed in prosthetic dentistry and the binary palladium gold alloys are also employed for swaged dentures. Rayon spinnerets have been made from the binary 20 and 30% palladium gold alloys, but the ternary platinum palladium gold alloys, the platinum gold alloys or the platinum rhodium alloys are superior to them for this purpose. The 40% palladium 60% gold alloy in conjunction with the 10% rhodium platinum alloy yields a high thermo-electric force and has found some use as a thermocouple. Various palladium gold alloys have been used for electrical contacts. Because of their narrow freezing range and nobility, palladium gold alloys are used for temperature limiting fuses. Palladium gold base alloys are also used for white platinum solders.

HYDROGEN PALLADIUM

An adequate summary of the wealth of complex and conflicting data available on the palladium hydrogen system is beyond the scope of this compilation. Smith (213), reviewing the literature on the system in 1939, suggested that stratification of phases, occasioned by the methods of preparation necessarily used, could account for the anomalies observed.

Studies have been made on palladium charged electrolytically, in which the maximum absorption approaches the ratio Pd_2H, and on palladium charged by exposure to molecular hydrogen in which, at high gas pressures, the absorption limit approaches PdH. Unlike most gas-metal systems, the solubility of hydrogen in palladium decreases with increase in temperature.

Of metallurgical interest, is the increase in hardness, tensile strength and electrical resistivity and the decrease in ductility and density of palladium resulting from the absorption of hydrogen. The marked effect of hydrogen on the mechanical properties of palladium was shown by Wise and Eash (27) who found that the tensile strength was raised from 30,000 lbs. per sq. in. to 48,000 lbs. per sq. in. and the elongation lowered from 38% in 2″ to 28% in 2″ by cooling in hydrogen from 800°C. The hardening of palladium resulting from the absorption of hydrogen is somewhat transient; it is rapidly lost in air or vacuo anneals at moderate temperatures, although it is not completely lost after five years at room temperature.

The very selective action of palladium in accepting hydrogen from miscellaneous hydrogen content atmospheres and transmitting it by diffusion has been made use of for years. One early application was in the old gas content X-ray tube which was often fitted with a small palladium thimble which was flamed with a small alcohol lamp when the tube got too "hard." The palladium "filtered" the hydrogen from the alcohol flame and admitted it to the evacuated chamber. This same general scheme has been used for providing considerable quantities of very pure hydrogen for special furnaces and functions very well. When supplied with electrolytic hydrogen these diffusers operate for long periods without attention. Provision must be made for continuous purging on the hydrogen supply side of the diffuser to avoid the accumulation of water vapor, nitrogen, etc., which are filtered out. Otherwise these residues would render the device inoperative after some time. A set-up employing this arrangement for the introduction of uncontaminated hydrogen into a furnace has recently been described by Gilfillan (214).

Figure 52 shows the effect of temperature on the rate of diffusion of hydrogen through a palladium septum 0.04 mm (0.0016″) thick with a differential hydrogen pressure of one atmosphere. A marked increase in the rate of diffusion with increase in temperature is evident. However, the diffusion rate decreases with time to a fairly constant value which is approximately two-thirds that of the initial rate. This decrease is more rapid at the higher temperatures, and operation of septa at 600°C causes a rapid and marked fall in the rate. Certain impurities in the hydrogen, such as sulphur compounds, are, of course, detrimental and should be eliminated.

Contrary to what might be expected, the diffusion of hydrogen through palladium appears to be proportional to

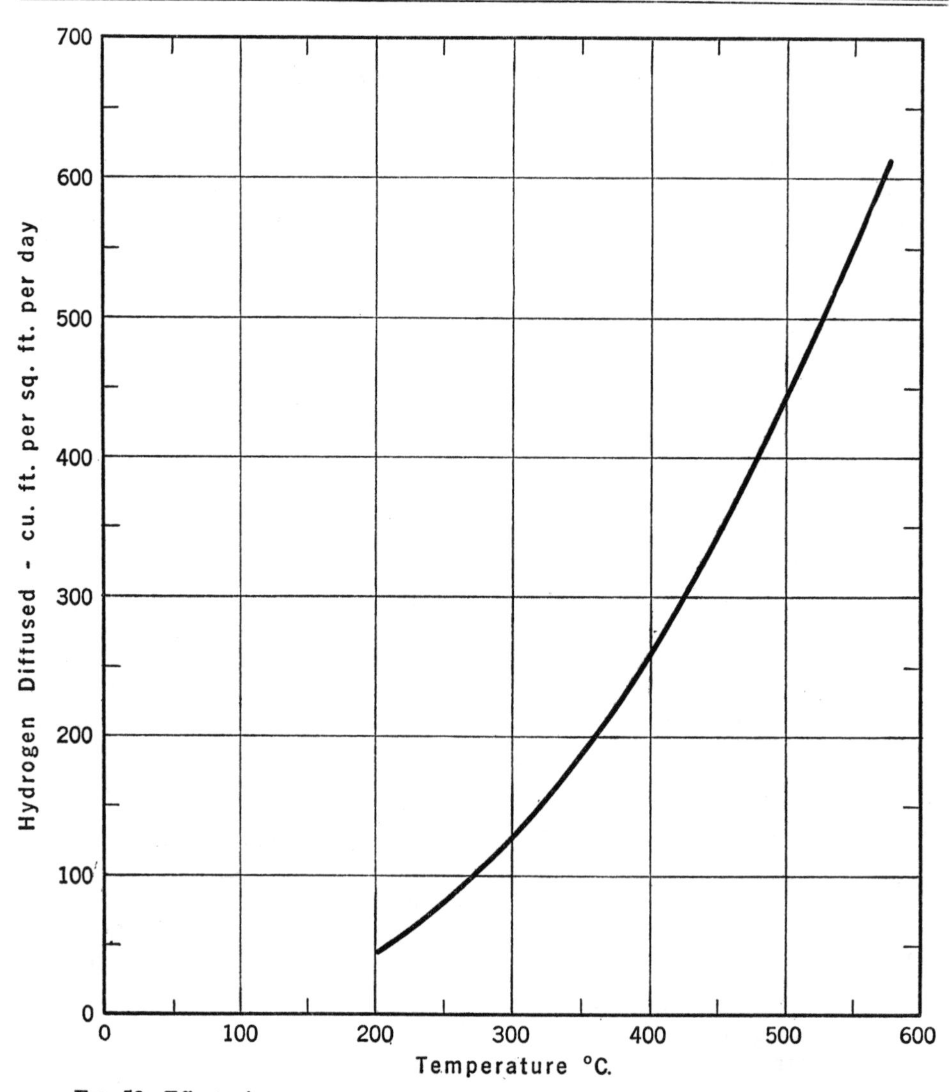

FIG. 52. *Effect of temperature on the rate of diffusion of hydrogen through a palladium septum* 0.04 *mm* (0.0016") *thick at a differential hydrogen pressure of one atmosphere.*

the pressure difference and not to the square root of the pressure difference, at least, for pressure differentials between 100 mm and 70 atmospheres.

IRIDIUM PALLADIUM

The equilibrium diagram of this system has not been determined.

ELECTRICAL PROPERTIES

Carter (17) reports the electrical resistivity of the 5, 10, 15 and 20% iridium alloys as 14.3, 23.3, 33.3 and 40 microhm-cm respectively.

MECHANICAL PROPERTIES

The Brinell hardness numbers for the 5, 10, 15 and 20% iridium alloys in the annealed condition are 70, 85, 125 and 155 respectively according to Carter (17).

WORKABILITY

Low iridium content alloys are readily workable but those containing more than about 20% iridium are difficult to work.

CORROSION AND TARNISH RESISTANCE

Iridium is quite effective in improving the corrosion and tarnish resistance of palladium. Alloys with 2% of iridium are resistant to the nitric acid drop test and alloys with 10% iridium are untarnished by industrial sulphur bearing atmospheres.

COLOR

The color of the workable alloys is similar to that of palladium.

USES

Iridium hardened palladium alloys have been used for jewelry purposes and are suitable for electrical contacts.

IRON PALLADIUM

Grigoriev's (158) work indicates that a continuous series of solid solutions crystallize from palladium iron melts. With the exception of a limited region at the iron end which is body centered cubic, the alloys are face centered cubic above about 900°C. The system, Figure 53, exhibits a minimum in the liquidus and solidus at about 34% (50 atomic percent) iron. The gamma high temperature solid solution forms two superlattices below about 800°C, one believed to be based on $FePd_3$ (14% iron) retaining a cubic lattice and the other based on FePd (34% iron) becoming tetragonal according to Hultgren and Zapffe (159) and Hocart and Fallot (183). The maxima of these ordered phases appear to be displaced from the simple atomic compositions of $FePd_3$ and FePd. Palladium shows little solubility in alpha iron and alloys containing more than about 40% iron are duplex. According to Hultgren and Zapffe (159), the alpha-gamma transformation occurs at increasingly higher temperatures as the iron content is increased. In alloys containing less than about 30% palladium the gamma phase cannot be preserved by quenching. Further work is required to determine the exact nature and compositional domain of the low temperature phases.

ELECTRICAL PROPERTIES

Resistivity values for this series of alloys have not been reported. According to Grigoriev (158), the temperature coefficient of electrical resistance (25-100°C) of alloys slowly cooled from 950°C increases from 0.00355 per °C for palladium to 0.00855 per °C for the 16% iron alloy and then falls to 0.00400 per °C at 69% iron after which it increases to 0.00692 per °C at 100% iron.

MECHANICAL PROPERTIES

Grigoriev (158) determined the Brinell hardness values of the entire series of alloys in the quenched and slowly cooled conditions, but his hardness curves show several unexplained abrupt changes. The hardness of the 15% iron alloy increases from about 98 BHN when quenched from 1000°C to about 140 BHN when slowly cooled.

USES

Certain of the palladium iron alloys may have unusual magnetic properties and it is probable that a composition with a low coefficient of expansion similar to that in the nickel iron system also exists.

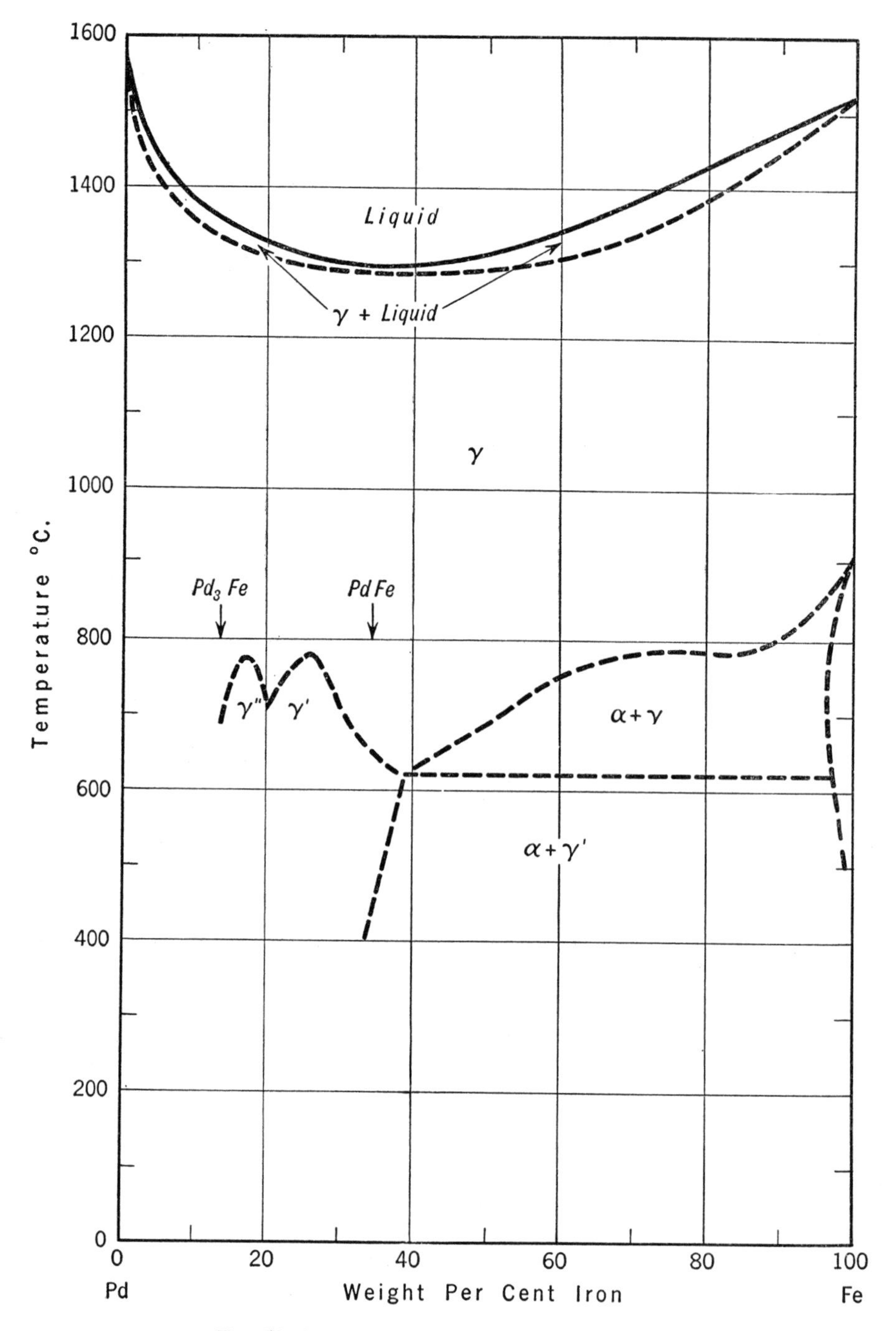

FIG. 53. *Iron-palladium constitutional diagram.*

LEAD PALLADIUM

Using thermal and microscopic methods, Ruer (164) investigated the palladium lead system, but only cursorily examined the palladium-rich end. He found a eutectic at 34% palladium and 1197°C between palladium and the compound Pd_3Pb (39% lead). Since the eutectic arrest was not observed in the 20% lead alloy, it is possible that the solid solubility of lead in palladium is in the neighborhood of 20% at the solidus temperature. Although this seems high, the 10% lead alloy appears to be a solid solution and does not show age hardening on slow cooling. The compound Pd_3Pb (39% lead) melts at 1220°C and several other compounds, including $PdPb_2$, PdPb and Pd_2Pb are formed by peritectic reactions at lower temperatures.

MECHANICAL PROPERTIES

From an investigation of the effect of impurities on palladium, Carter (51) reported the properties shown in Table 46 for palladium and 0.1% lead palladium alloy worked under exactly comparable conditions.

TABLE 46
Properties of Palladium and 0.1% Lead-Palladium Alloy

	Palladium	0.1% Lead Palladium
Brinell Hardness		
Hard..........	74	92
Annealed......	43	57
Tensile Strength, Lbs. per sq. in.		
Hard..........	37,000	50,000
Annealed......	19,000	25,000

The 10% lead palladium alloy has a Vickers hardness of 110 when annealed at 1000°C and 210 when cold rolled 50%. It is ductile and does not age harden on slow cooling from 1000°C.

MANGANESE PALLADIUM

The rather complicated system is shown in Figure 54. The palladium manganese alloys containing up to about 46.5% manganese crystallize as a face centered cubic solid solution, according to Grube and Winkler (161) and Grube, Bayer and Bumm (162), in spite of the fact that the liquidus and solidus have a sharp minimum at 21.3% manganese and a maximum at 34% manganese. Between 46.5 and 66% manganese an eutectic is formed, the eutectic point being at 57.5% manganese and 1147°C. Two other solid solutions are formed at still higher manganese contents.

The palladium rich solid solution undergoes two solid transformations; one based on Pd_3Mn_2 beginning at 1175°C and 25.6% manganese, and the other based upon PdMn beginning at about 610°C and 34% manganese. Both of these transformations involve a change from the face centered cubic to the tetragonal lattice. Transformations in higher manganese content alloys, which are shown in the diagram, are complicated by the allotropic changes of manganese (163) (184).

ELECTRICAL PROPERTIES

According to Grube, Bayer and Bumm (162), the electrical resistivity at 20°C increases rapidly from 11 microhm-cm for palladium to 96 microhm-cm at 34% manganese. At this point a sharp break occurs in the curve and the resistivity increases very rapidly, finally reaching a maximum of 330 microhm-cm at 82% manganese.

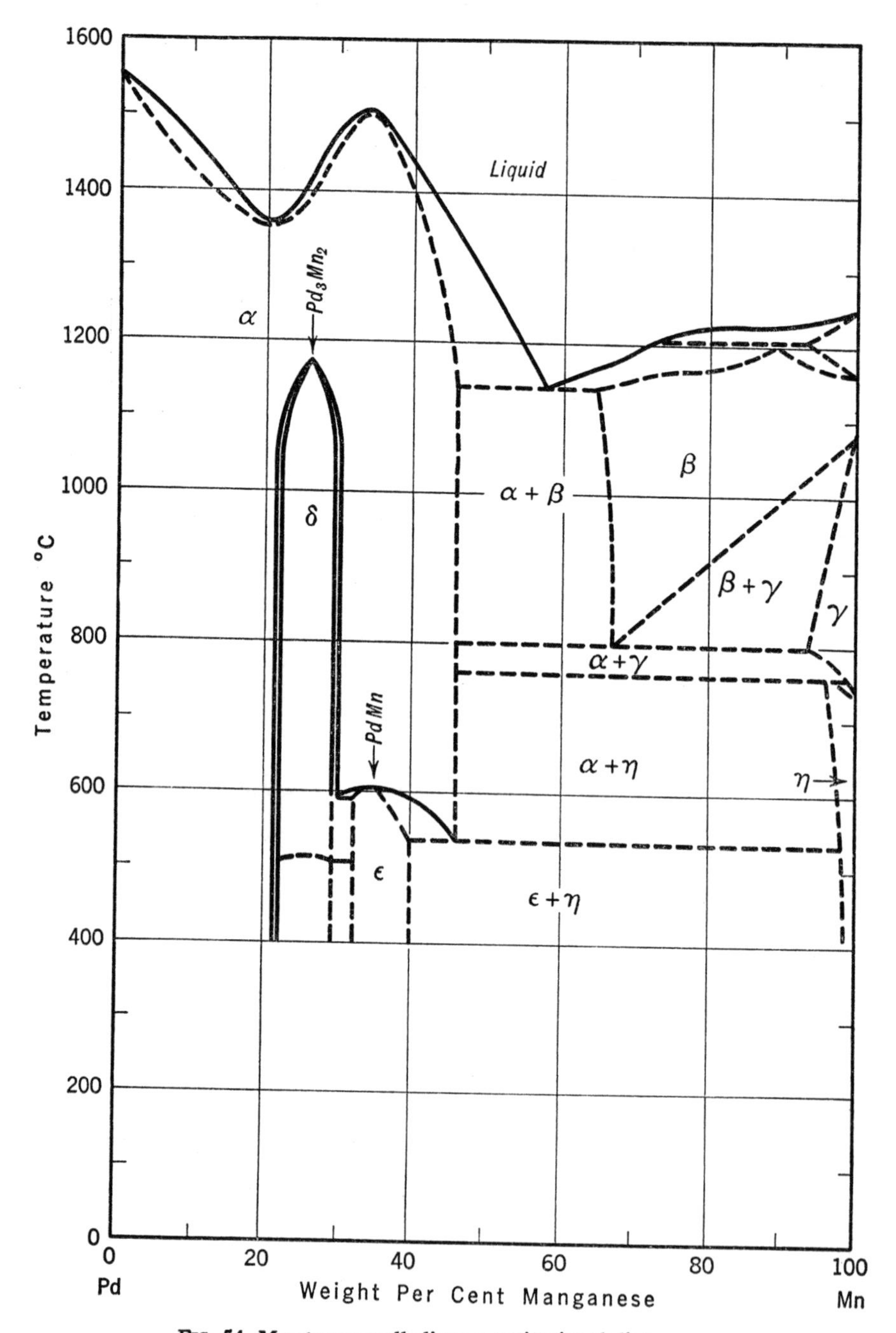

FIG. 54. *Manganese-palladium constitutional diagram.*

MECHANICAL PROPERTIES

According to Grube, Bayer and Bumm (162), the Brinell hardness of the palladium-rich alloys, after quenching from 1100°C, increases from 38 BHN for palladium to an intermediate maximum of 84 BHN at 5% manganese, then falls to about 62 BHN at about 24% manganese after which it increases to a maximum of about 180 BHN at 50% manganese. Alloys within this range do not age harden significantly on slow cooling from 1000°C. These investigators also report a rather high maximum hardness of about 700 BHN for the 90% manganese alloy in the cast or slowly cooled condition.

Wise and Vines (173) obtained the values shown in Table 47 for the palladium-rich alloys.

TABLE 47
Properties of Palladium-Manganese Alloys

Weight % Manganese	VHN		Tensile Strength Lbs. per sq. in. Annealed
	Cold Rolled 50%	Annealed	
5	171	85	......
15	248	116	61,200

WORKABILITY

Alloys with up to about 15% manganese have good working properties but above 25% manganese they are brittle.

USES

With sufficiently pure manganese, these alloys may be useful for electrical contacts and for spark plug electrodes. With the further addition of gold, silver and copper, they may provide tarnish resistant dental alloys of adequate ductility and castability.

NICKEL PALLADIUM

It is evident, from the work of Heinrich (153) and Fraenkel and Stern (154) that a continuous series of solid solutions crystallize from palladium nickel melts, but whether this solid solution remains stable at lower temperatures is open to question. The solidification diagram, Figure 55, shows a minimum in liquidus and solidus at about 40% nickel and since other binary systems of this type show solid transformations, similar reactions in the solid state are to be expected in this system. Although Fraenkel and Stern concluded from unreported work that there is a transformation in the solid state, Hultgren and Zapffe (159) report, from lattice determinations, that the system is devoid of transformations in the solid state. Hardness values of annealed and aged alloys are practically identical (173), but further work concerning possible solid transformations is indicated.

ELECTRICAL PROPERTIES

Little is known of the electrical properties of these alloys. Grigoriev (155) determined the temperature coefficient of electrical resistance for the whole series of alloys, but the plotted results show several unexplained abrupt changes.

MECHANICAL PROPERTIES

The Brinell hardness values for the entire series of alloys in the annealed condition are shown in Figure 56. A maximum hardness of about 205 BHN occurs at about 35% (50 atomic percent) nickel. The alloys do not harden on aging at 450°C (173).

WORKABILITY

The ductility of these alloys is good if they are free from sulphur and other impurities.

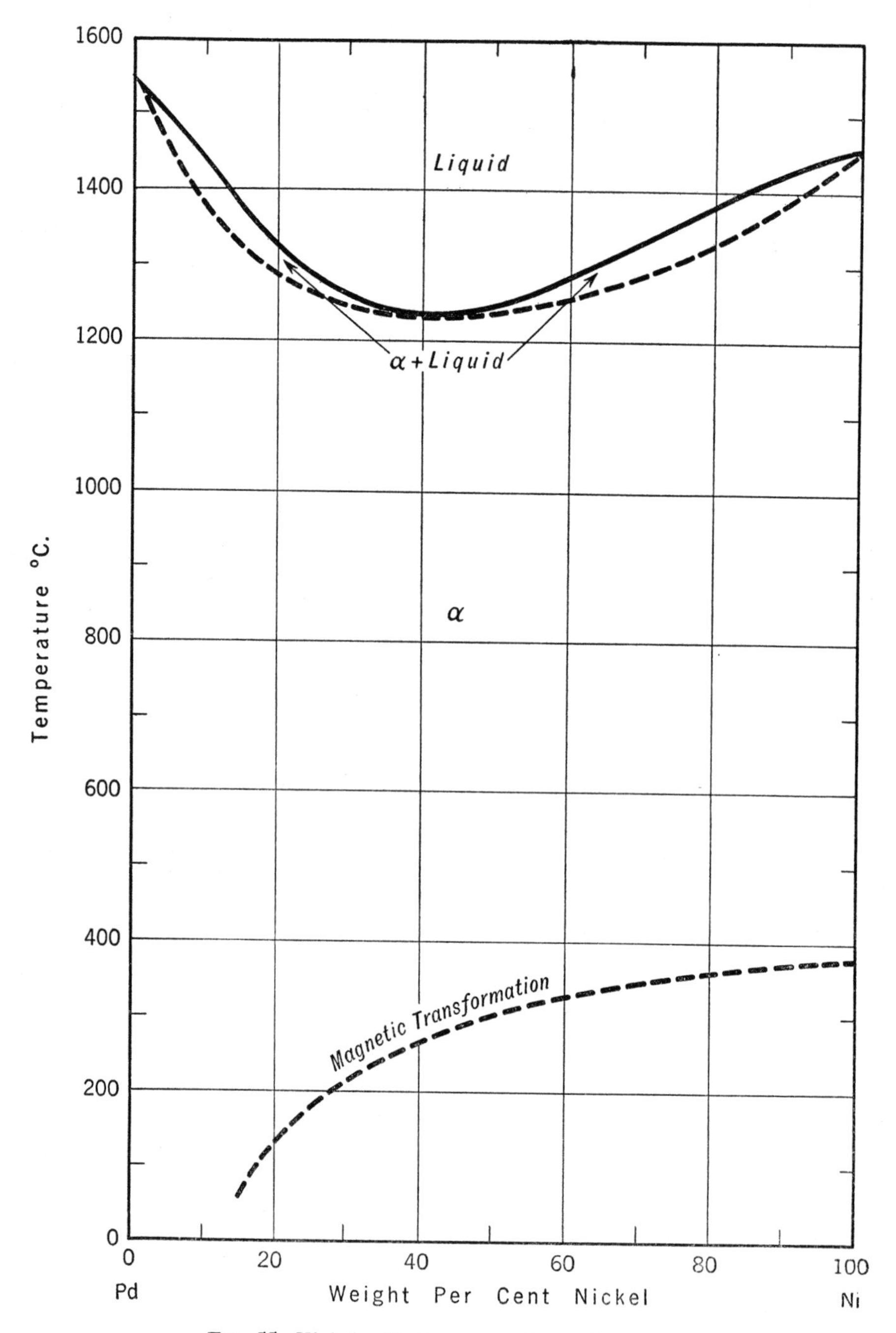

Fig. 55. ***Nickel-palladium constitutional diagram.***

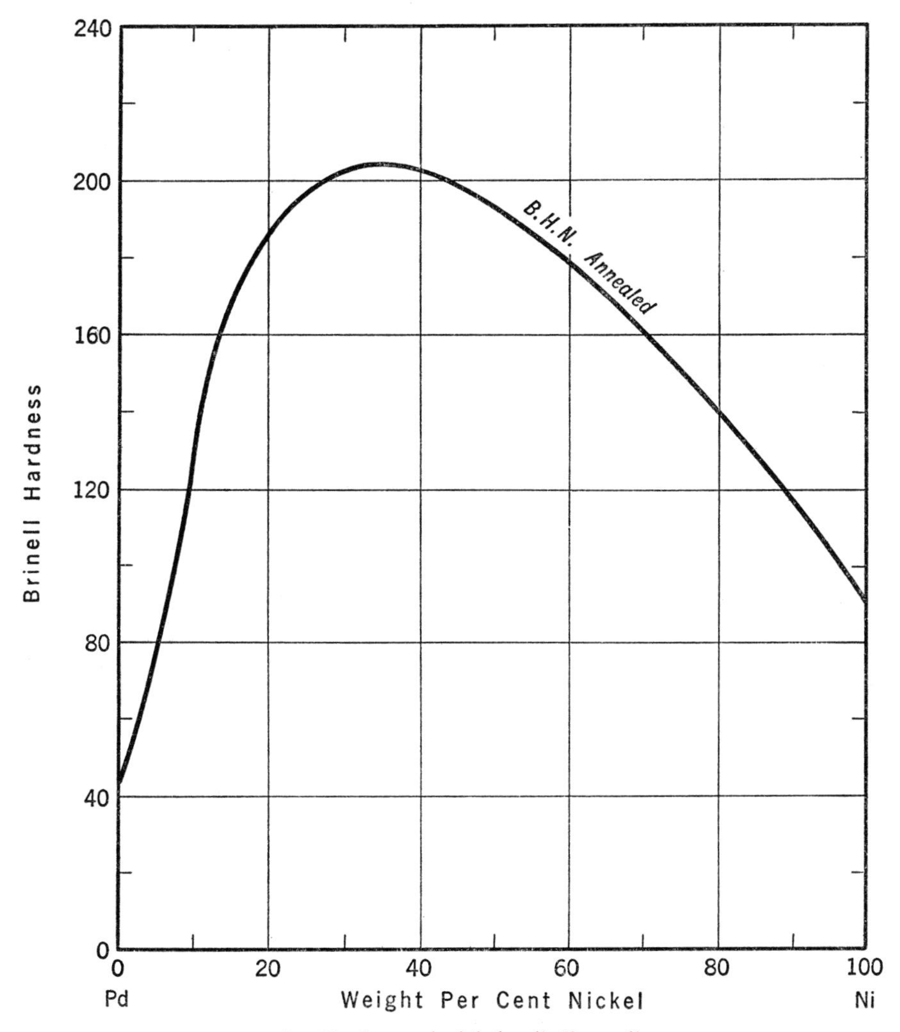

FIG. 56. *Hardness of nickel-palladium alloys.*

CORROSION AND TARNISH RESISTANCE

The corrosion and tarnish resistance of the binary palladium nickel alloys is intermediate between that of the component metals and can be raised to levels above those of gold alloys by the addition of platinum, rhodium or iridium in quantities of from 5 to 20%.

COLOR

All alloys are substantially white.

USES

Palladium nickel alloys have been suggested as suitable for electrical contacts and could also be employed for jewelry.

OSMIUM PALLADIUM

The equilibrium diagram of this system has not been determined but since the metals belong to different crystallographic systems, it is not expected to be of the simple solid solution type.

ELECTRICAL PROPERTIES

Carter (17) has reported the electrical resistivity of the 5, 10 and 25% osmium alloys to be 16.6, 20 and 20 microhm-cm respectively.

MECHANICAL PROPERTIES

The Brinell hardnesses of the 5, 10, 15, 20 and 25% osmium alloys in the annealed condition are 65, 80, 100, 127 and 160 BHN respectively according to Carter (17).

WORKABILITY

Alloys containing more than about 10% osmium are difficult to work.

CORROSION AND TARNISH RESISTANCE

The corrosion and tarnish resistance of the workable alloys is probably superior to that of pure palladium.

COLOR

The color of the palladium-rich alloys approaches that of palladium.

PHOSPHORUS PALLADIUM

Wiehage, Weibke and Biltz (167) examined the system up to 35% phosphorus by thermal, microscopic and X-ray methods. They found that the addition of phosphorus to palladium rapidly reduced the liquidus temperature to 807°C at 5.5% phosphorus, at which point the compound Pd_5P was formed by a peritectic reaction. This compound and Pd_3P (8.7% phosphorus) which melts at 1047°C form an eutectic melting at 788°C and containing 6.4% phosphorus. Another eutectic at 795°C and 12.33% phosphorus occurs between Pd_5P_2 (10.5% phosphorus), which is formed by a peritectic reaction at 860°C, and PdP_2 which melts at 1150°C. The solid solubility of phosphorus in palladium has not been determined but from the work of Jedele (131) it is believed to be below 0.01% phosphorus at the solidus temperature. However, Wiehage, Weibke and Biltz (167) report that the alloys with up to about 4% phosphorus are relatively ductile, which is surprising.

MECHANICAL PROPERTIES

Jedele (131) found that small percentages of phosphorus in palladium increased the hardness and tensile strength but decreased the ductility. He reported 75 BHN, 40,000 lbs. per sq. in. tensile strength and 19.5% elongation for the 0.265% phosphorus alloy as compared with 50 BHN, 31,900 lbs. per sq. in. tensile strength and 23.1% elongation for palladium. He also determined the tensile strength of the low phosphorus content alloys at 850°C and found that alloys containing more than 0.006% phosphorus were brittle at 850°C.

WORKABILITY

Although Wiehage, Weibke, and Biltz say that alloys with up to 4% phosphorus are relatively tough, Jedele was unable to work the 0.93% phosphorus alloy. This difference may be due to the use of different working or annealing temperatures.

COLOR

Wiehage, Weibke and Biltz report that alloys with up to 4% phosphorus are more silvery than leaden in color while those with more than 7% phosphorus are lead color.

RHODIUM PALLADIUM

Tammann and Rocha (134) concluded, from a study of the microstructure of rapidly solidified and annealed alloys, that the liquidus and solidus curves rise from the melting point of palladium to that of rhodium and that the two metals form an unbroken series of solid solutions. The Brinell hardness values of annealed alloys are in accord with the conclusion, but further work is required to prove the absence of low temperature phases.

ELECTRICAL PROPERTIES

According to Carter (17) the electrical resistivity of the 10% rhodium alloy in the annealed state is 26 microhm-cm.

MECHANICAL PROPERTIES

The Brinell hardness values of annealed alloys, based mainly upon the work of Tammann and Rocha (134), are shown in Figure 57. A maximum hardness of about 145 BHN occurs at about 60% rhodium. The hardness values of hard rolled alloys containing up to 15% rhodium are also shown in the same figure. The 15% rhodium alloy age hardens slightly, increasing from 78 BHN to 110 BHN on aging at 550°C.

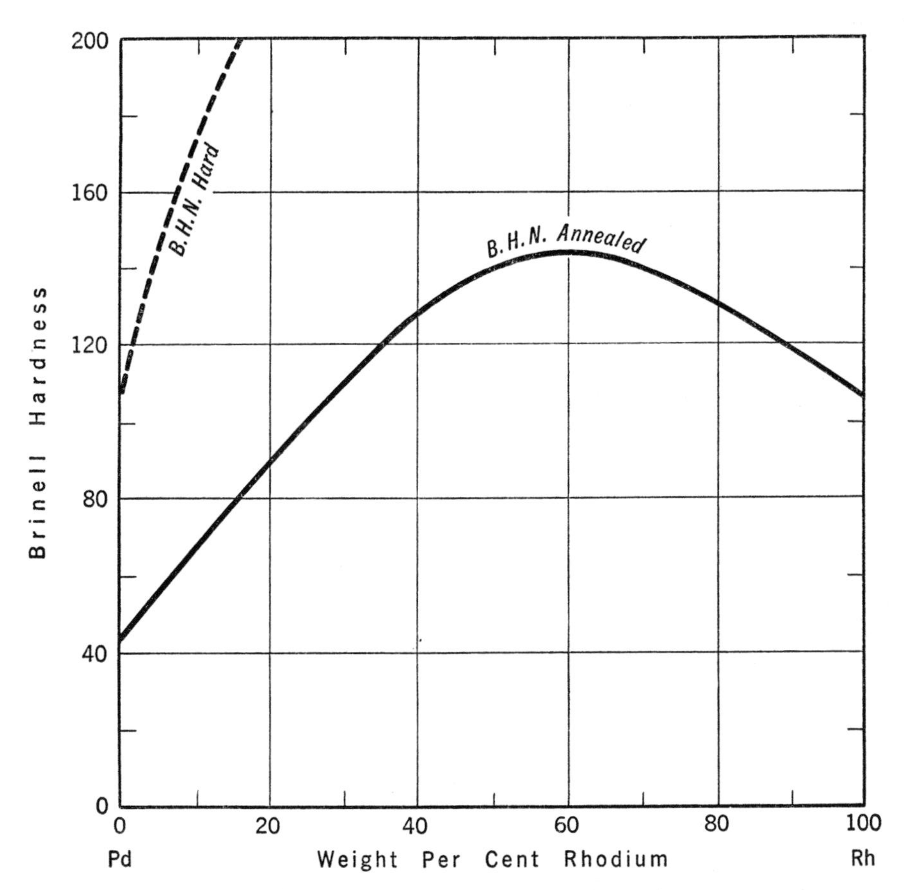

FIG. 57. *Hardness of rhodium-palladium alloys.*

WORKABILITY

The ductility of alloys containing more than 20% rhodium is quite low and those containing more than 25% rhodium are unworkable. Whether the low ductility of these alloys is due to a brittle rhodium phase or to impurities in the rhodium employed has not yet been determined.

CORROSION AND TARNISH RESISTANCE

Rhodium, like iridium, markedly improves the nobility of palladium. When tested by the nitric acid drop test, the 2% rhodium alloy is as resistant as 14 Kt. jewelry gold and the 10% rhodium alloy is completely resistant. The 10% rhodium alloy is also resistant to tarnish by industrial sulphur-bearing atmospheres.

COLOR

The ductile alloys containing up to 20% rhodium have the color of palladium and as the rhodium content is increased the color whitens to that of rhodium.

USES

Rhodium-palladium alloys containing up to about 10% rhodium, usually with some ruthenium as a hardener, have been used for denture bases and jewelry.

RUTHENIUM PALLADIUM

The equilibrium diagram of this system has not been investigated but since the metals belong to different crystallographic systems, the formation of an unbroken series of solid solutions would not be expected.

MECHANICAL PROPERTIES

Hardness values for annealed and cold worked palladium ruthenium alloys containing up to 15% ruthenium, as reported by Carter (51), are given in Table 48. He also reports the tensile strength of the 5% ruthenium alloy as 54,000 lbs. per sq. in. when annealed and 85,000 lbs. per sq. in. when cold worked.

TABLE 48
Brinell Hardness of Palladium-Ruthenium Alloys

Weight Per Cent Ruthenium	Brinell Hardness	
	Hard	Annealed
4	110	90
5	152	90
7.5	230	130
10	249	169
11	248	195
12	248	203
15	...	238

WORKABILITY

The limit of workability has not been definitely determined but appears to be close to 15% ruthenium.

CORROSION AND TARNISH RESISTANCE

The corrosion and tarnish resistance of alloys containing up to 10% ruthenium is somewhat better than that of palladium.

COLOR

All the workable alloys have the color of palladium.

USES

Ruthenium palladium alloys, usually containing some rhodium or copper, are used for jewelry.

SILICON PALLADIUM

The work of Lebeau and Jolibois (168) suggests that an eutectic between palladium and the compound Pd_2Si occurs at about 670°C and 6% silicon. Pd_2Si (11.62% silicon) melts at about 1400°C and is practically insoluble in solid palladium. Small amounts of silicon in palladium and many of its alloys reduce the ductility and cause hot shortness due to the formation of the brittle low melting eutectic. Palladium-rich alloys should not be melted under reducing conditions when in contact with siliceous material since silica is reduced and enters the melt under such circumstances.

SILVER PALLADIUM

The palladium silver system is believed to be of the simple solid solution type free from transformations in the solid state. The liquidus and solidus lie close together and descend smoothly from the melting point of palladium to that of silver as shown in the equilibrium diagram, according to Ruer (141), in Figure 58. Measurements of electrical resistivity, temperature coefficient of electrical resistance, thermal conductivity, mechanical properties and lattice constants by various investigators all confirm the conclusion that the system is devoid of transformations in the solid state, although the shape of the resistivity composition curve is somewhat peculiar and questions have been raised

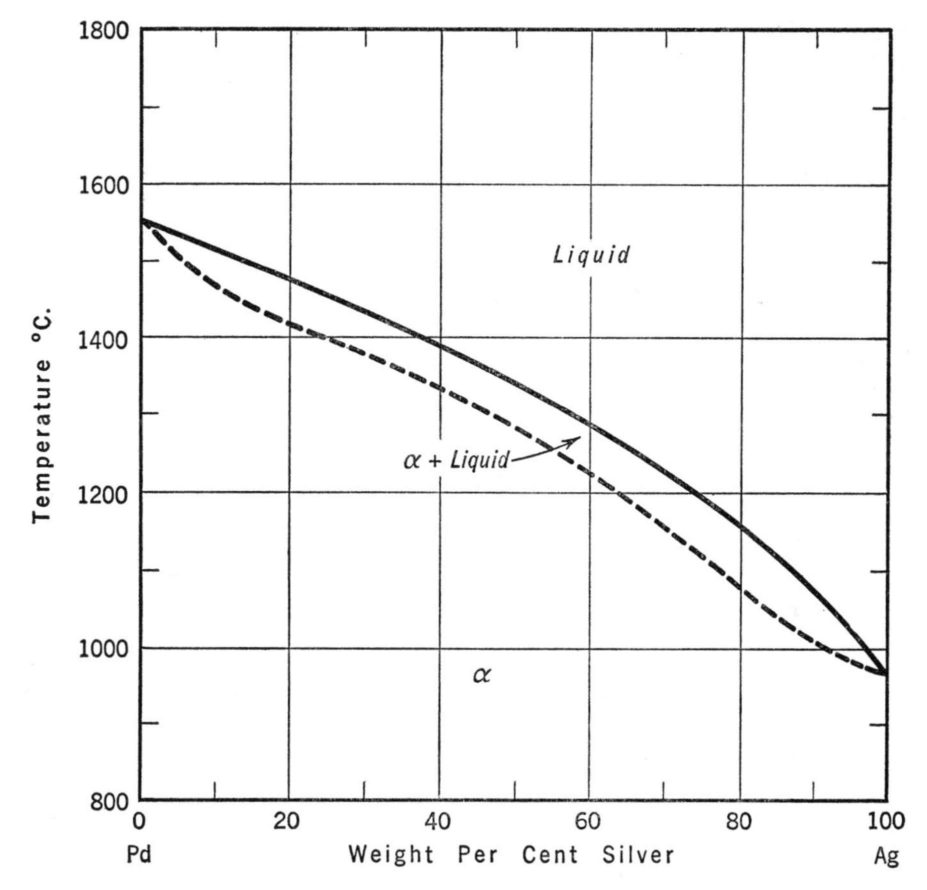

FIG. 58. *Silver-palladium constitutional diagram.*

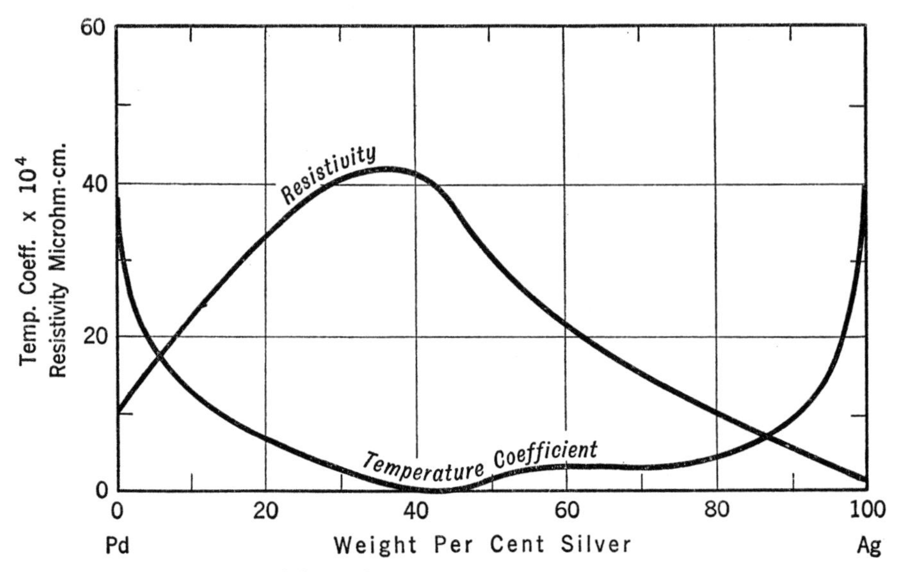

FIG. 59. *Electrical resistivity and temperature coefficient of silver-palladium alloys.*

as to whether the system is as simple as most of the properties indicate.

ELECTRICAL PROPERTIES

Electrical resistivities obtained by Geibel (87), Wise (109), Carter (17 and 51), Schulze (88), Sedstrom (106) and Svensson (142) on palladium silver alloys agree closely and place the maximum resistivity of 42 microhm-cm at about 40% silver, as shown in Figure 59. The temperature coefficient of electrical resistance reaches a very low value of 0.00002 per °C (0-100°C) at 44% silver according to Carter (51). The peculiar change in slope of the electrical resistivity and temperature coefficient curves in the neighborhood of 50% silver has not been explained.

MECHANICAL PROPERTIES

Hardness values for cold worked and annealed alloys are shown in Figure 60. Maxima of about 100 BHN in the annealed state and 180 BHN in the cold worked (66% reduction) condition are obtained at 30% silver. Tensile strength values show similar maxima of 55,000 lbs. per sq. in. annealed and 99,000 lbs. per sq. in. cold worked (50% reduction) for the 30% silver alloy.

WORKABILITY

The ductility of all palladium silver alloys is high and they are readily worked.

CORROSION AND TARNISH RESISTANCE

Alloys containing more than about 50% palladium approach palladium in resistance to tarnish and corrosion. The lower palladium content alloys are usually ennobled with platinum or gold to improve their tarnish resistance. The entire series of alloys is of course attacked by nitric acid, but in alloys containing more than about 40% palladium complete resistance to this reagent can be obtained by the addition of about 10% of platinum (145).

COLOR

All alloys are substantially white in color although on the whole they are somewhat darker than the end members.

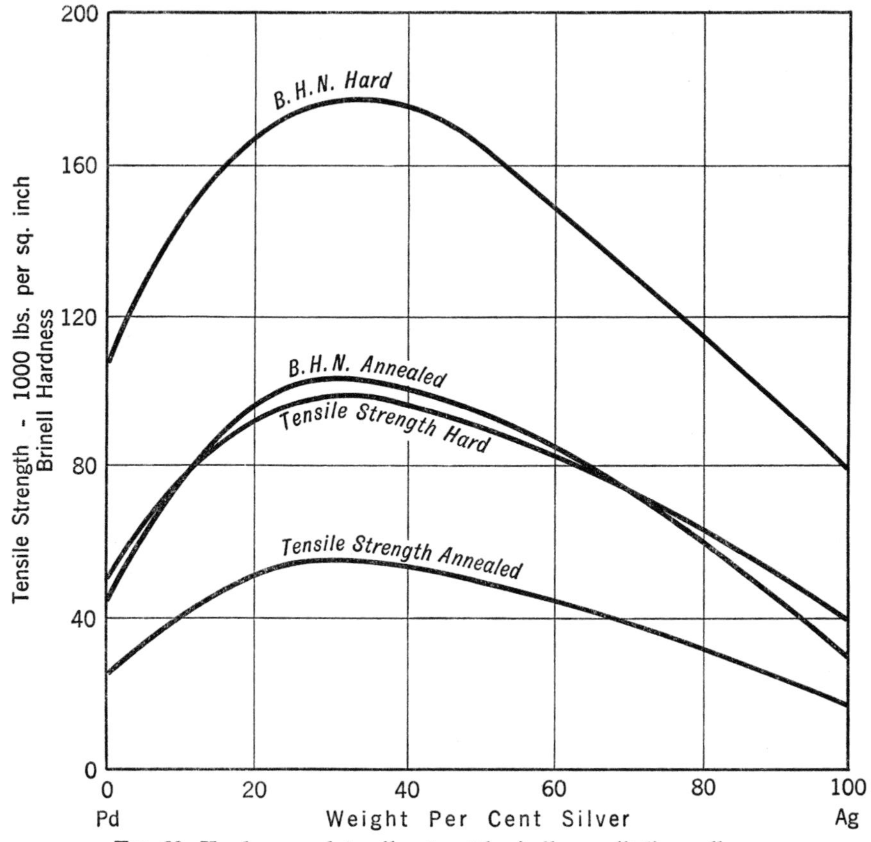

Fig. 60. ***Hardness and tensile strength of silver-palladium alloys.***

USES

The 50% palladium alloy, preferably with up to 10% of platinum, is suitable for jewelry, watch cases and optical frames where its white color and corrosion resistance are desired. This and other higher palladium alloys have also been used for wrought denture bases. Lower palladium content alloys, usually ennobled with small amounts of platinum or gold and hardened with copper, zinc or tin, are used in Europe for both wrought and cast dental appliances and for fountain pen nibs. The 60% palladium alloy is used for electrical contacts operating at reasonably high currents, while alloys containing a few percent of palladium are also employed for contacts in low voltage relays and regulators. Alloys containing 10 or 20% palladium have been used in Europe instead of corresponding gold silver alloys for electrical contacts in telephone and telegraph relays. The low temperature coefficient of electrical resistivity makes the 56% palladium silver alloy of interest for special resistors where its reasonably high resistivity, very low temperature coefficient of resistivity, and its excellent corrosion resistance and good contact performance are valuable. This alloy has a strain sensitivity $\Delta R/R/\Delta L/L$ of 0.885 as compared with 2.06 for Constantan and may be useful for resistance type strain gauges where a more corrosion resistant material than Constantan is required.

SULPHUR PALLADIUM

The palladium-rich portion of this system has been investigated by Raper and Rhodes (170) and Weibke and Laar (171). According to these investigators, sulphur rapidly reduces the liquidus temperature to 761°C at 7% sulphur at which point a peritectic reaction leading to the formation of the compound Pd_4S takes place as shown in Figure 61. Jedele's (131) work indicates that the solubility of sulphur at 850°C is less than 0.01% sulphur and it is probable that at room temperature the solid solubility is less than 0.005% sulphur. The compounds PdS (23.1% sulphur and Pd_4S (7% sulphur) form a phase at about 10.4% sulphur which, at 554°C, undergoes an eutectoidal transformation. Alloys with more than about 11% sulphur separate into two layers on solidification.

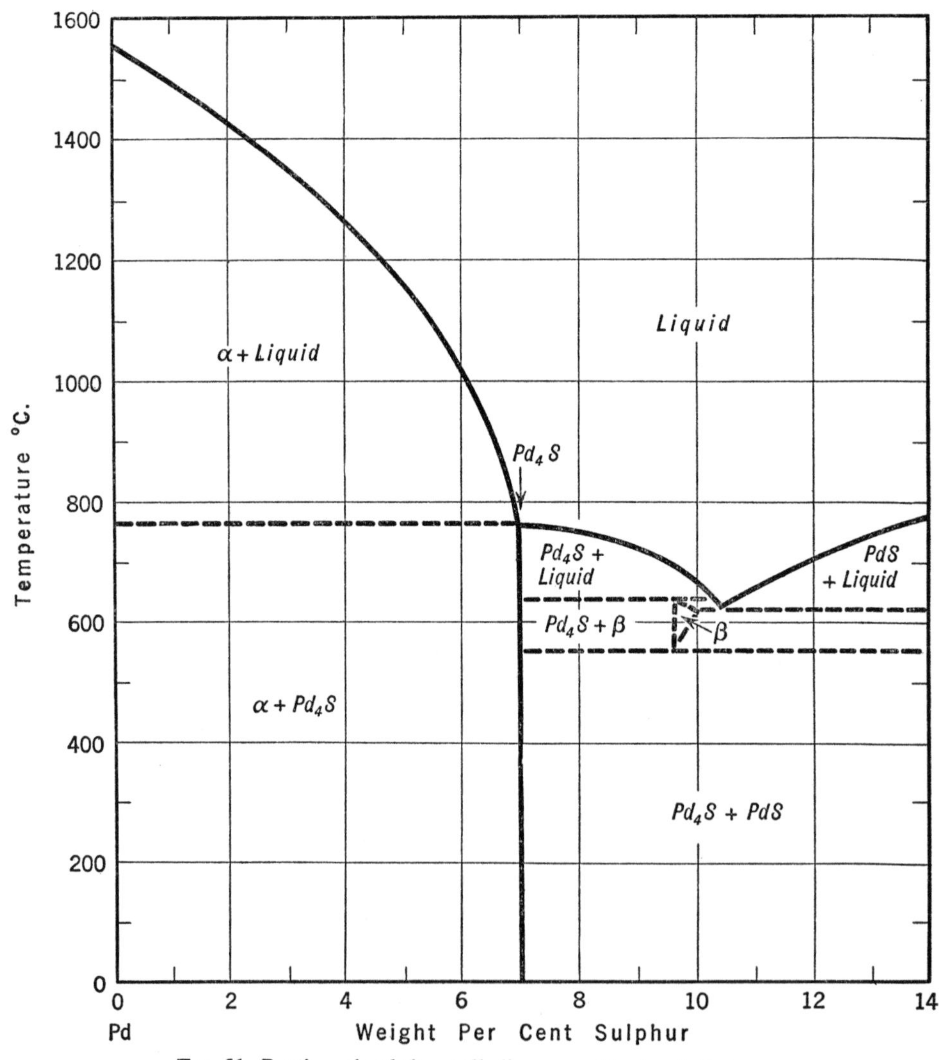

FIG. 61. *Portion of sulphur-palladium constitutional diagram.*

MECHANICAL PROPERTIES

Jedele (131) found that small percentages of sulphur in palladium increased the hardness and tensile strength, but decreased the ductility. He obtained 65 BHN, 41,900 lbs. per sq. in. tensile strength and 17.2% elongation for a 0.32% sulphur alloy, as compared with 50 BHN, 31,900 lbs. per sq. in. tensile strength and 23.1% elongation for palladium. The 0.92% sulphur alloy had a Brinell hardness of 90 BHN but was brittle. He also determined the tensile strength of the low sulphur content alloys at 850°C and found that alloys containing more than 0.005% sulphur were brittle at this temperature, presumably because of the presence of a trace of a molten phase.

RHODIUM ALLOYS

COPPER RHODIUM

The rhodium copper system was studied by Zviagintzev and Brunovskiy (212). According to these investigators, terminal solid solutions form in the range 0-6% copper and 70 to 100% copper, the intermediate range being duplex. X-ray studies showed the presence of superlattice lines in alloys with 17.4, 38.2 and 65.6% copper and indicate the existence of the compounds Rh_3Cu, RhCu and $RhCu_3$.

GOLD RHODIUM

From the results of an X-ray investigation, Drier and Walker (204), concluded that the solid solubility of gold in rhodium is of the order of 2.5% gold. They also estimate the solid solubility of rhodium in gold to be between 2 and 5% rhodium. The exact nature of the intermediate duplex region has not been determined.

NICKEL RHODIUM

This system has not been investigated in detail but is believed to be analogous to the platinum nickel system.

MECHANICAL PROPERTIES

The Vickers hardness, after annealing at 1000°C, is 195 VHN at 33% nickel and decreases with increase in nickel content; being 165 VHN at 57% nickel and 140 VHN at 70% nickel. From these data it appears that the hardness curve for this system is similar to that of the palladium nickel system and has a maximum in the neighborhood of 35% nickel. Tensile data on the highly corrosion resistant 57% nickel alloy and similar alloys containing molybdenum which are useful for pen nibs are given in Table 49.

WORKABILITY

The ductility of the alloys containing more than about 30% nickel is good, and they can be readily worked if free from impurities such as sulphur.

TABLE 49
Mechanical Properties of Rhodium-Nickel Alloys

	Tensile Strength Lbs. per sq. in.		Proportional Limit Lbs. per sq. in.		Elongation Per Cent in 2 inches	
	Hard	Annealed	Hard	Annealed	Hard	Annealed
43% Rh, 57% Ni	173,600	98,000	111,500	37,600	2.25	52
42.6% Rh, 55.4% Ni, 2.0% Mo	186,700	105,000	123,500	49,600	3.0	43.5
42.2% Rh, 53.9% Ni, 3.9% Mo	191,000	109,500	119,000	51,300	2.5	38

CORROSION AND TARNISH RESISTANCE

Because the nobility of rhodium is high and its atomic weight is low, exceptional resistance to tarnish and corrosion is obtained at rather low weight percentages of rhodium. The 35% rhodium alloy is completely resistant to tarnish in industrial atmospheres and to corrosion by nitric acid or ferric chloride solution.

COLOR

Alloys with up to about 40% rhodium are similar to nickel in color but above 40% rhodium they become progressively whiter with increase in rhodium content.

USES

Because of its complete resistance to corrosion from writing fluids, its high strength and modulus of elasticity, the 35% rhodium alloy is suitable for fountain pen nibs (186).

SILVER RHODIUM

An X-ray and microscopic examination of this system by Drier and Walker (204) indicated a solid solubility of about 0.1% silver in rhodium, and insolubility of rhodium in silver. The nature of the intermediate duplex region has not been reported.

REFERENCES

1. Ninth Report of the Committee on Atomic Weights
Jnl. Am. Chem. Soc. V. 61 (1939) 223

2. Kahlbaum, G. W. A. and E. Strum
Z. anorg. allg. Chem. V. 46 (1905) 242

3. Owen, E. A. and E. L. Yates
Phil. Mag. V. 15 (1933) 472

4. Roeser, W. F., F. R. Caldwell and H. T. Wensel
Jnl. Res. Bur. Stds. V. 6 (1931) 1119

5. Hoffmann, F. and C. Tingwaldt
Phys. Zeit. V. 35 (1934) 434

6. Schofield, F. H.
Proc. Roy. Soc. A 146 (1934) 792

7. Jones, H. A., I. Langmuir and G. M. J. MacKay
Phys. Rev. V. 30 (1927) 201

8. Crookes, W.
Proc. Roy. Soc. A 86 (1912) 461

9. Stewart, W.
Wied. Ann. V. 66 (1898) 90

10. Holborn, L. and L. W. Austin
Phil. Mag. V. 7 (1904) 388

11. Jaeger, W. and H. Diesselhorst
Wiss. Abh. Phys. Tech. Reichsanst. V. 3 (1900) 269, 415

12. Barrat, T. and R. M. Winter
Proc. Phys. Soc. V. 26 (1914) 347

13. Holborn, L. and A. L. Day
Ann. Physik. V. 4 (1901) 104

14. Holborn, L., K. Scheel and F. Henning
Warmetabellen. Braunschweig. (1919) 54

15. Jaeger, F. M., E. Rosenbohm and J. A. Bottema
Proc. Akad. Amsterdam V. 35 (1932) 763

16. Roeser, W. F.
U. S. Bur. Stds. Private Communication

17. Carter, F. E.
Trans. Am. Inst. Min. & Metallurg. Eng. V. 78 (1928) 759
Japan Nickel Review V. 4 (1936) 21-28, 134-151

18. Goedecke, W.
Festschrift 50 *jahrigen, Siebert G.M.B.H., Hanau, Germany* (1931) 72

19. Caldwell, F. R.
Jnl. Res. Bur. Stds. V. 10 (1933) 275

20. Holborn, L. and A. L. Day
Sitzber. Akad, Berlin (1899) 694
Ann. Physik. V. 2 (1900) 505

21. Honda, K. and Y. Shimizu
Nature V. 132 (1933) 565

22. Coblentz, W. W.
Jnl. Franklin Inst. V. 170 (1910) 169, 183
Bull. Bur. Stds. V. 5 (1908) 182, 198, 369

23. Henning, F.
Zeit. Instrkd. V. 30 (1910) 72

24. Jones, F. L.
Bausch and Lomb Optical Co., Private Communication

25. Atkinson, R. H. and A. R. Raper
Electrodepositors Tech. Soc. V. 9 (1934) 77

26. Sivil, C. S.
Baker and Co. Private Communication

27. Wise, E. M. and J. T. Eash
Trans. Am. Inst. Min. & Metallurg. Eng. V. 117 (1935) 313

28. Wise, E. M. and J. T. Eash
Trans. Am. Inst. Min. & Metallurg. Eng. V. 128 (1938) 282

29. Stauss, H. E.
Trans. Am. Inst. Min. & Metallurg. Eng. V. 137 (1940) 474

30. Wegel, R. L.
Bell Telephone Laboratories, Private Communication

31. Sivil, C. S.
Trans. Am. Inst. Min. & Metallurg. Engs. V. 93 (1931) 246

32. Jaeger, F. M. and E. Rosenbohm
Proc. Akad. Amsterdam. V. 33 (1930) 457

33. Jaeger, F. M. and W. A. Veenstra
Proc. Akad. Amsterdam V. 37 (1934) 280

34. Jaeger, F. M. and J. E. Zanstra
Proc. Akad. Amsterdam V. 34 (1931) 15

35. Schofield, F. H.
Proc. Roy. Soc. A V. 155 (1936) 301

36. Fairchild, C. O., W. H. Hoover and M. F. Peters
Jnl. Res. Bur. Stds. V. 2 (1929) 931

37. Morris, L. D. and S. R. Scholes
Jnl. Amer. Cer. Soc. V. 18 (1935) 359

38. Richardson, D.
Spectroscopy in Sci. and Ind. Mass. Inst. Tech., J. Willey & Sons (1938) 64

39. Mott, W. R.
Trans. Amer. Electrochem. Soc. V. 34 (1918) 225

40. Holzmann, H.
Festschrift 50 *jahrigen, Siebert G.M.B.H., Hanau, Germany* (1931) 147

41. Grube, G. and R. Knabe
Z. Electrochem. V. 42 (1936) 793

42. Grube, G. and H. Kastner
Z. Electrochem. V. 42 (1936) 156

43. Connybeare, J. G. G.
Proc. Roy. Soc. V. 49 (1937) 29-37

44. Schofield, F. H.
Proc. Roy. Soc. V. 155 (1936) 301

45. Holborn, L.
Ann. Physik. V. 59 (1919) 145

46. Shimizu, Y.
Sci. Rep. Tohoku Univ. V. 21 (1932) 826, 864

47. Honda, K.
Ann. Physik. V. 32 (1910) 1027

48. von Wartenberg, H.
Verh. deut. Phys. Ges. V. 12 (1910) 105

49. Kenworthy, L.
National Physical Laboratory, Private Communication

50. Atkinson, R. H. and A. R. Raper
Electrodepositors Tech. Soc. V. 8 (1933)

51. Carter, F. E.
Baker & Co., Private Communication

52. Schaffer, C.
Zeit. Physik. V. 17 (1923) 152

53. Gruneisen, E.
Ann. Physik. V. 26 (1908) 397

54. Holborn, L., F. Henning and L. Austin
Wiss. Abh. Phys. Tech. Reichsanst. V. 4 (1903) 227

55. Henning, F. and H. T. Wensel
Jnl. Res. Bur. Stds. V. 10 (1933) 809

56. Barrat, T. and R. M. Winter
Ann. Physik. V. 77 (1925) 5

57. Holborn, L. and S. Valentiner
Ann. Physik. V. 22 (1907) 16

58. Jaeger, F. M. and E. Rosenbohm
Proc. Akad. Amsterdam V. 34 (1931) 808

59. Holborn, L.
Ann. Physik. V. 59 (1919) 165

60. Holborn, L. and A. L. Day
Ann. Physik. V. 2 (1900) 505

61. Owen, M.
Ann. Physik. V. 37 (1912) 657

62. Nemilow, W. A.
Annals Inst. Platine (U.S.S.R.) V. 7 (1929) 13-20
Z. anorg. allg. Chem. V. 204 (1932) 41-48

63. Rydberg, I. R.
Zeit. Phys. Chem. V. 33 (1900) 357

64. Edwards, C. A.
Metal Ind. (Lond.) V. 18 (1921) 221

65. Atkinson, R. H.
Mond Nickel Co., Acton Refinery, Private Communication

66. Jaeger, F. M. and E. Rosenbohm
Proc. Akad. Amsterdam 34 (1931) 85

67. Roeser, W. F. and H. T. Wensel
Jnl. Res. Bur. Stds. V. 12 (1934) 519

68. Wohler, L. and W. Muller
Z. anorg. allg. Chem. V. 149 (1925) 125

69. Ebert, H.
Phys. Zeit. V. 39 (1938) 6

70. Swanger, W. H.
Jnl. Res. Bur. Stds. V. 3 (1929) 1029

71. Gruneisen, E.
Z. Physik. V. 44 (1927) 642

72. Acken, J. S.
Jnl. Res. Bur. Stds. V. 12 (1934) 249

73. Brenner, B.
Ind. and Eng. Chem. V. 27 (1935) 438

74. Honda, K.
Ann. Physik. V. 31 (1910) 149

75. Coblentz, W. W. and R. Stair
Jnl. Res. Bur. Stds. V. 22 (1939) 93

76. Mirror Dept. Cir.
Heraeus G.M.B.H., Hanau, Germany 1938

77. Nemilow, W. A. and N. M. Voronow
Annals Inst. Platine (U.S.S.R.) (1935) 35
Z. anorg. allg. Chem. V. 226 (1936) 201-208

78. Atkinson, R. H. and A. R. Raper
Electrodepositors Tech. Soc. V. 9 (1934) 77

79. Joly, A. and M. Vezes
Compt. Rend. V. 116 (1893) 577

80. Owen, E. A., L. Pickup and I. O. Roberts
Z. Krist V. 91 (1935) 70

81. Fizeau, H.
Compt. Rend. V. 68 (1869) 1129, 1175

82. Blau, F.
Electrotech. Zeit. V. 25 (1905) 198

83. Lombardi, L.
Electrotech. Zeit. V. 25 (1905) 42

84. Honda, K. and T. Sone
Sci. Rep. Tohoku Univ. V. 2 (1913) 26

85. Benedicks, C.
Z. Metallkde. V. 7 (1915) 225

86. Honda, K.
Ann. Physik. V. 32 (1910) 1027

87. Geibel, W.
Z. anorg. allg. Chem. V. 70 (1911) 242-54

88. Schulze, F. A.
Physik. Zeit. V. 12 (1911) 1028-31

89. Feussner, O. and L. Muller.
Heraeus Festschrift, Heraeus G.M.B.H., Hanau, Germany (1930) 1-17
Ann. Physik. V. 7 (1930) 9-47

90. Nowack, L.
Z. Metallkde. V. 22 (1930) 94-103

91. Stienmann, E.
Compt. Rend. V. 130 (1900) 819

92. Sosman, R. B.
Am. Jnl. Sci. V. 30 (1910) 1

93. Day, A. L. and R. B. Sosman
Am. Jnl. Sci. V. 33 (1912) 33

94. Adams, L. H.
Jnl. Am. Chem. Soc. V. 36 (1914) 65

95. Roeser, W. F. and H. T. Wensel
Jnl. Res. Bur. Stds. V. 10 (1933) 275

96. Caldwell, F. R.
Jnl. Res. Bur. Stds. V. 10 (1933) 373

97. Ageew, N. W. and V. G. Kusnezov
Izvest. Akad. Nauk., S.S.S.R. (Bull. Acad. Sci., U.S.S.R.) V. 4 (1937) 753-755

98. Nemilow, W. A. and A. A. Rudnizky
Izvest. Akad. Nauk., S.S.S.R. (Bull. Acad. Sci., U.S.S.R.) V. 1 (1937) 33-38

99. Doerinckel, F.
Z. anorg. allg. Chem. V. 54 (1907) 333-358

100. Grigoriev, A. T.
Annals Inst. Platine (U.S.S.R.) V. 6 (1938) 184-194
Z. anorg. allg. Chem. V. 178 (1929) 97-107

101. Johansson, C. H. and J. O. Linde
Ann. Physik. V. 5 (1930) 762-793

102. Stenzel, W. and J. Weerts
Z. Metallkde. V. 24 (1932) 139-40
Festschrift 50 *jahrigen, Siebert G.M.B.H., Hanau, Germany* (1931) 288

103. Wise, E. M. and W. S. Crowell
Trans. Amer. Inst. Min. & Metallurg. Eng. V. 99 (1932) 365

104. Kurnakow, N. S. and W. A. Nemilow
Z. anorg. allg. Chem. V. 168 (1928) 339-348

105. Johansson, C. H. and J. O. Linde
Ann. Physik V. 6 (1930) 458-86
(Erratum) Ann. Physik. V. 7 (1930) 408

106. Sedstrom, E.
Dissertation, Stockholm 1924

107. Johansson, C. H. and J. O. Linde
Ann. Physik. V. 82 (1927) 449-79

108. Kurnakow, N. S. and W. A. Nemilow
Z. anorg. allg. Chem. V. 210 (1933) 1-12
Annals Inst. Platine (U.S.S.R.) V. 8 (1931) 5-16

109. Wise, E. M.
International Nickel Co., Unpublished Research.

110. Kurnakow, N. S. and W. A. Nemilow
Annals Inst. Platine (U.S.S.R.) V. 8 (1931) 17-24
Z. anorg. allg. Chem. V. 210 (1933) 13-20

111. Nemilow, W. A.
Z. anorg. allg. Chem. V. 213 (1933) 283-291

112. Constant, F. W.
Physical Rev. V. 36 (1930) 786 *and* 1654

113. Jellinghouse, W.
Z. Techn. Physik. V. 17 (1936) 33

114. Isaac, E. and G. Tammann
Z. anorg. allg. Chem. V. 55 (1907) 63-71

115. Graf, L. and A. Kussmann
Physik Zeit. V. 36 (1935) 544-51

116. Kussmann, A.
Physik. Zeit. V. 38 (1937) 41-42

117. Nemilow, W. A.
Z. anorg. allg. Chem. V. 204 (1932) 49-59
Annals Inst. Platine (U.S.S.R.) V. 7 (1929) 1-12

118. Aallot, F.
Bull. Soc. Franc. Phys. V. 360 (1934) 146

119. Nemilow, V. and I. Voronow
Ann. Sectur Platine (U.S.S.R.) V. 14 (1937) 157

120. Muller, L.
Ann. Physik. V. 7 (1930) 9

121. Kremer, D.
Abh. Inst. Metallhutt. Electromet. Techn. Hochsch. Aa Chem V. 6 (1916) 18

122. Kussmann, A. and E. Friederich
Physik. Zeit. V. 36 (1935) 185
Z. Metallkde. V. 26 (1934) 119

123. Nemilow, W. A.
Z. anorg. allg. Chem. V. 218 (1934) 33

124. Podkopajew, N.
Jnl. russ phys. chem. Ges. V. 40 (1908) 249
Chem. Zbl. V. 2 (1908) 493

125. Doerinckel, F.
Z. anorg. allg. Chem. V. 54 (1908) 358-65

126. Raper, A. R. and A. B. Middleton
Mond Nickel Co., Acton Refinery, Private Communication

127. Friederich, K. and A. Leroux
Metallurgie V. 6 (1909) 1

128. Nemilow, V. A. and N. M. Voronow
Ann. Inst. Platine (U.S.S.R.) V. 12 (1935) 17-25
Z. anorg. allg. Chem. V. 226 (1936) 177-184

129. Friederich, K. and A. Leroux
Metallurgie V. 5 (1908) 148

130. Biltz, W., F. Weibke, E. May and K. Meisel
Z. anorg. allg. Chem. V. 223 (1935) 129

131. Jedele, A.
Z. Metallkde V. 27 (1935) 271

132. Collier, L. J., T. H. Harrison and W. G. A. Taylor
Trans. Faraday Soc. V. 30 (1934) 581

133. Voronow, N. M.
Ann. Secteur Platine (U.S.S.R.) V. 13 (1936) 145-166

134. Tammann, G. and H. J. Rocha
Festschrift 50 *jahrigen, Siebert G.M.B.H., Hanau, Germany,* (1931) 309-320

135. Ruer, R.
Z. anorg. allg. Chem. V. 51 (1906) 391-96

136. Fraenkel, W. and A. Stern
Z. anorg. allg. Chem. V. 166 (1927) 166

137. Geibel, W.
Z. anorg. allg. Chem. V. 69 (1911) 43-46

138. Rohl, H.
Ann. Physik V. 18 (1933) 155

139. Johansson, C. H.
Ann. Physik V. 76 (1925) 452

140. Holgerson, S. and E. Sedstrom
Ann. Physik V. 75 (1924) 149-150

141. Ruer, R.
Z. anorg. allg. Chem. V. 51 (1906) 315-319

142. Svensson, B.
Ann. Physik V. 14 (1932) 699-711

143. McKeehan, L. W.
Physics Rev. V. 20 (1922) 424

144. Kruger, F. and G. Gehm
Ann. Physik V. 16 (1933) 190-193

145. Wise, E. M.
U. S. Patent No. 2,129,721

146. Ruer, R.
Z. anorg. allg. Chem. V. 51 (1911) 223-230

147. Taylor, R.
Jnl. Inst. Met., Lond. V. 54 (1934) 255

148. Jones, F. W. and C. Sykes
Jnl. Inst. Met., Lond. V. 65 (1939) 419

149. Johansson, C. H. and J. O. Linde
Ann. Physik V. 78 (1925) 454-57
V. 82 (1927) 449-58

150. Bragg, W. L., C. Sykes, and A. J. Bradley
Proc. Roy. Soc. V. 49 (1937) 96

151. Belogonov, P. S.
Metallurgist (U.S.S.R.) V. 6 (1936) 92

152. Stockdale, D.
Trans. Faraday Soc. V. 30 (1934) 310-314

153. Heinrich, F.
Z. anorg. allg. Chem. V. 82 (1913) 322

154. Fraenkel, W. and A. Stern
Z. anorg. allg. Chem. V. 166 (1927) 164-166

155. Grigoriev, A. T.
Ann. Inst. Platine (U.S.S.R.) V. 9 (1932) 13-22

156. Grube, G. and H. Kastner
Z. Electrochem. V. 42 (1936) 156

157. Grube, G. and O. Winkler
Z. Electrochem. V. 41 (1935) 52

158. Grigoriev, A. T.
Z. anorg. allg. Chem. V. 209 (1932) 295

159. Hultgren, R. and C. Zapffe
Trans. Am. Inst. Min. Metallurg. Eng. V. 133 (1939) 58

160. Grube, G. and R. Knabe
Z. Electrochem. V. 42 (1936) 793

161. Grube, G. and O. Winkler
Z. Electrochem. V. 42 (1936) 815

162. Grube, G., K. Bayer and H. Bumm
Z. Electrochem. V. 42 (1936) 805

163. Grube, G. and O. Winkler
Z. Electrochem. V. 45 (1939) 784-787

164. Ruer, R.
Z. anorg. allg. Chem. V. 52 (1907) 345

165. Grigoriev, A. T.
Z. anorg. allg. Chem. V. 209 (1932) 308

166. Sander, W.
Z. anorg. allg. Chem. V. 75 (1912) 97

167. Wiehage, G., F. Weibke and W. Biltz
Z. anorg. allg. Chem. V. 228 (1936) 357

168. Lebeau, P. and P. Jolibois
Compt. Rend. V. 146 (1908) 1028

169. Thompson, J. F. and E. H. Miller
Jnl. Am. Chem. Soc. V. 28 (1906) 1115-1132

170. Raper, A. R and E. C. Rhodes
Mond Nickel Co., Acton Refinery, Private Communication

171. Weibke, L. and J. Laar
Z. anorg. allg. Chem. V. 224 (1935) 49

172. Carter, F. E. and H. E. Stauss
Metals Handbook Am. Soc. Metals (1939) 1691

173. Wise, E. M. and R. F. Vines
International Nickel Co., unpublished research.

174. Linde, J. O.
Ann. Physik V. 30 (1937) 151-164

175. Kussmann, A. and H. Nitka
Physikal Zeit. V. 39 (1938) 373-375

176. Kussmann, A. and H. Nitka
Metallwirtschaft V. 17 (1938) 657

177. Hildebrand, E.
Ann. Physik V. 30 (1937) 593-608

178. Nemilow, V. A., T. A. Vidusova and M. N. Pivovarova
Izvest. Akad. Nauk., S.S.S.R. (Bull. Acad. Sci., U.S.S.R.) V. 4 (1937) 743-752

179. Zintl, E. and H. Kaiser
Z. anorg. allg. Chem. V. 211 (1933) 113-131

180. Fischer, J.
Chem. Fabrik V. 35 (1938) 406-408

181. Reeve, H. T.
Bell Telephone Laboratories, Private Communication

182. Seemann, H. J.
Naturwiss V. 24 (1936) 618-619

183. Hocart, R. and M. Fallot
Compt. rend. V. 204 (1937) 1465-1467

184. Grigoriev, A. T.
Anal. Inst. Anal. Phys. Chem. (U.S.S.R.) V. 7 (1935) 75-87

185. Siebert, G.
German Patent No. 652,034

186. Wise, E. M. and R. F. Vines
U. S. Patent No. 2,066,870

187. Wise, E. M. and R. F. Vines
Trans. Amer. Inst. Min. Met. Eng. V. 137 (1940) 464

188. Auwarter, M.
Zeitschr. f. techn. Physik V. 18 (1927) 457-459

189. Esser, H., W. Eilender and K. Bungardt
Arch Eisenhuttenw V. 12 (1938) 157

190. Jaeger, F. and E. Rosenbohm
Physica V. 6 (1939) 1123

191. Roeser, W. F. and H. T. Wensel
"Temperature—Its Measurement and Control in Science and Industry"
Reinhold Publishing Corp., N. Y. (1941) 1293-1326

192. Stephans, R. E.
Jnl. Opt. Soc. Amer. V. 29 (1939) 158

193. Hoge, H. J. and F. G. Brickwedde
Jnl. Res. Bur. Stds. V. 22 (1939) 351-373

194. Meissner, W.
Ann. Physik. V. 29 (1937) 264

195. Owen, E. A. and J. I. Jones
Proc. Phys. Soc. V. 49 (1937) 587

196. Greenslade, G. R.
Jnl. Heat. Piping and Air Conditioning, Jan. 1931

197. Barber, C. R. and F. H. Schofield
Proc. Roy. Soc. A. V. 173 (1939) 117

198. Auwarter, M.
J. Applied Physics V. 10 (1939) 705-710

199. Carter, F. E.
Trans. Amer. Electrochem. Soc. V. 43 (1923) 397

200. Rhodes, E. C.
Mond Nickel Co., Acton Refinery, Private Communication

201. Wise, E. M.
U. S. Pats. 1,913,423 *and* 1,935,897

202. Winkler, O.
Z. Metallkde. V. 30 (1938) 162-173

203. Sieverts, A. and K. Bruning
Z. Physik. Chem. V. 168 (1934) 412

204. Drier, R. W. and H. L. Walker
Phil. Mag. V. 16 (1933) 294-298

205. Waidner, C. W. and G. K. Burgess
Bull. Nat. Bur. Stds. V. 3 (1907) 163

206. Mendenhall, C. E.
Astrophys. Jnl. V. 33 (1911) 91

207. McCauley, G. V.
Astrophys. Jnl. V. 37 (1913) 164

208. Henning, F. and H. Heuse
Z. Physik. V. 16 (1923) 63

209. Honda, K.
Ann. Physik. V. 32 (1910) 1027

210. Honda, K.
Sci. Rep. Tohoku Imp. U. V. 1 (1912) 1

211. Pearson, G. L.
U. S. Pat. 2,184,847

212. Zviagintzev, O. E. and B. K. Brunovskiy
Ann. Inst. Platine V. 12 (1935) 37

213. Smith, D. P.
Trans. Electrochem. Soc. V. 78 (1940) 117-130

214. Gilfillan, E. S.
Trans. Electrochem. Soc. V. 77 (1940) 43-48

215. Gebhardt, E. and W. Koster
Z. Metallkde. V. 38 (1940) 262

216. Gebhardt, E. and W. Koster
Z. Metallkde. V. 38 (1940) 253

217. Masing, G., K. Eckhardt and K. Kloiber
Z. Metallkde. V. 38 (1940) 122

218. Neumann, H.
Archiv. Technisches Messen No. 69 (1937) *T.* 38

219. Martin, D. L. and Geisler, A. H.
Jnl. App. Physics, V. 22 (1921) 290-298

SELECTED BIBLIOGRAPHY

GENERAL

A COMPREHENSIVE TREATISE ON INORGANIC AND THEORETICAL CHEMISTRY.
Volumes 15 and 16. Palladium, Rhodium, Ruthenium, Iridium, Osmium and Platinum. *J. W. Mellor, Longmans and Co., New York* 1937.

GMELINS HANDBUCH DER ANORGANISCHEN CHEMIE.
Volumes on Platinum, Ruthenium, Osmium and Palladium. *Verlag Chemie G.m.b.H. Berlin* 1939.

MODERN USES OF NON FERROUS METALS, Edited by C. H. Matthewson. Chap. on Platinum Metals by *E. M. Wise, Amer. Inst. Min. Met. Eng. New York* 1935.

PLATINUM AND ALLIED METALS:
Some Points of Interest to the Chemical Engineer. *C. H. Johnson and R. H. Atkinson Trans. Inst. Chem. Eng. (London) v.* 15 (1937) 131-144.

FESTSCHRIFT ZUM 70 GEBURTSTAGE
W. C. Heraeus, Hanau, Germany 1930

FESTSCHRIFT ZUM 50 JAHRIGEN BESTEHEN DER PLATINSCHMELZE
G. Siebert, Hanau, Germany, 1931

HISTORY

PLATINUM
D. McDonald
Chem. and Ind. (London) V. 50 (1931) 1931-41

PLATINUM
P. M. Tyler and R. M. Santmyers
Bur. Mines Information Circ. #6389 (1931)

THE DISCOVERY OF THE ELEMENTS VIII THE PLATINUM METALS
M. E. Weeks
Jnl. Chem. Educ. V. 9 (1932) 1017-1034

ON THE DISCOVERY OF PALLADIUM
A. M. White and H. B. Friedman
Jnl. Chem. Educ. V. 9 (1932) 236-245

DISCOVERY AND EARLY HISTORY OF PLATINUM IN RUSSIA
B. N. Menshutkin
Jnl. Chem. Educ. V. 11 (1934) 226-9

STATISTICS

THE MINERALS YEAR BOOK
U. S. Bur. Mines. (*Annual*)

THE MINERAL INDUSTRY (*Annual*)

PLATINUM AND ALLIED METALS
Imperial Institute, Mineral Resources Dept., London, 1936

REFINING

METALS OF THE PLATINUM GROUP: Ores, Recovery and Refining, Fabrication and Uses and Properties
R. H. Atkinson and A. R. Raper
Jnl. Inst. Metals (London) V. 59 (1936) 179-206

PURIFICATION OF THE SIX PLATINUM METALS
E. Wichers, R. Gilchrist and W. H. Swanger
Trans. Amer. Inst. Min. Met. Engs. V. 76 (1928) 602

REFINING AND MELTING SOME PLATINUM METALS
J. O. Whiteley and C. Dietz
Trans. Amer. Inst. Min. Met. Engs. V. 76 (1928) 635

REFINING PRECIOUS METAL WASTES
C. M. Hoke
Metallurgical Publishing Co., New York 1940

ANALYSIS

A PROCEDURE FOR THE SEPARATION OF THE SIX PLATINUM METALS FROM ONE ANOTHER AND FOR THEIR GRAVIMETRIC DETERMINATION
R. Gilchrist and E. Wichers
Jnl. Amer. Chem. Soc. V. 57 (1935) 2565-2573

THE ASSAY OF THE PLATINUM METALS
F. E. Beamish and J. J. Russell
Ind. & Eng. Chem. (Anal. Ed.) V. 8 #2 (1936) 141-44

NEW PROCEDURE FOR THE ANALYSIS OF DENTAL GOLD ALLOYS
R. Gilchrist
Research Paper R. P. 1103, Jnl. Res. Bur. Stds. V. 20 (1938) 745-771

ANALYSIS OF DENTAL GOLD ALLOYS
W. H. Swanger
Bur. Stds. Sci. Paper 532 (1926)

APPLIED INORGANIC ANALYSIS
W. F. Hillebrand and G. E. F. Lundell
John Willey and Sons, N. Y. 1929

SCOTTS STANDARD METHODS OF CHEMICAL ANALYSIS—Fifth Edition
N. H. Furman
D. Van Nostrand and Co. N. Y. 1939

MELTING AND WORKING

FABRICATION OF THE PLATINUM METALS
C. S. Sivil
Trans. Amer. Inst. Min. Met. Engrs. V. 93 (1931) 244-260

MELTING, MECHANICAL WORKING AND SOME PHYSICAL PROPERTIES OF RHODIUM
W. H. Swanger
Jnl. Res. Bur. Stds. V. 3 (1929) 1029-1040

VACUUM CASTING (of Platinum)
H. T. Reeve
Metals and Alloys V. 2 (1931) 184-185

MELTING OF PLATINUM
C. M. Hoke
Metal Industry (NY) V. 34 (1936) 433-5, 468-70

ELECTRODEPOSITION

ELECTRODEPOSITION OF PLATINUM: Historical and General Review
R. H. Atkinson
Electrodepositors Tech. Soc. V. 13 (1937)

PLATING METALS OF THE PLATINUM GROUP: Platinum Palladium Rhodium
K. Schumpelt
Plating and Finishing Guidebook Metal Industry N. Y. (1939)

DEVELOPMENTS IN THE ELECTRODEPOSITION OF THE PLATINUM METALS
K. Schumpelt
Electrodepositors Tech. Soc. V. 13 (1937)

PLATINUM PLATING FROM ALKALINE SOLUTIONS
E. C. Davies and A. R. Powell
Electrodepositors Tech. Soc. V. 13 (1937)

ELECTRODEPOSITION OF RHODIUM
R. H. Atkinson and A. R. Raper
Electrodepositors Tech. Soc. V. 9 (1934) 77-82

THE ELECTRODEPOSITION OF PALLADIUM
R. H. Atkinson and A. R. Raper
Electrodepositors Tech. Soc. V. 8 (1933)

RHODIUM PLATING PROPERTIES, APPLICATIONS, PLATING PRACTICE AND COSTS
A. Bregman
The Iron Age V. 144 (1939) 31-33

UBER DIE ELEKTROLYTISCHE ABSCHEIDUNG DES RHODIUMS
E. Grube and E. Kesting
Zeit. fur Electrochemie V. 39 #12 (1933) 948-58

RHODIUM PLATING
C. G. Fink and G. C. Lambros
Trans. Amer. Electrochem. Soc. V. 63 (1933) 181-6

COATING BY SPUTTERING OR VAPORATION IN VACUO

CATHODE SPUTTERING—A COMMERCIAL APPLICATION (An extensive Bibliography on Cathode Sputtering of Metals is included)
H. F. Fruth
Physics V. 2 (1932) 280-288

RHODIUM MIRRORS FOR SCIENTIFIC PURPOSES
M. Auwarter
Jnl. Applied Physics V. 10 (1939) 705-710

SPUTTERED PALLADIUM FILMS
S. Tanaka
Tokyo Univ. Aeronaut. Res. Inst. Rept. #142 (1936) 369-406

CORROSION RESISTANCE

PLATINUM-CLAD EQUIPMENT
L. C. Burman
Chemical & Metallurgical Eng. V. 48 (1941) 89-90

PRECIOUS METALS AS MATERIALS OF CONSTRUCTION
F. E. Carter
Amer. Inst. Chem. Engs. V. 31 (1935) 459-72

THE SERVICEABILITY OF PLATINUM WARE OF VARIOUS COMPOSITIONS
R. Gilchrist and E. Wichers
Amer. Chem. Soc. 1935

PLATINUM IN THE CHEMICAL INDUSTRY
Baker and Co., Newark, N. J. 1939

THE HANDLING OF CORROSIVE GASES
T. H. Chilton and W. Huey
Ind. Eng. Chem. V. 24 (1932) 125-131

FRANGIBLE DISKS AS PROTECTION FOR PRESSURE VESSELS
M. E. Bonyun
Trans. Amer. Inst. Chem. Engs. V. 31 (1934-35) 256-277
Chem. Met. Eng. V. 42 (1935) 260

QUESTIONS RELATING TO APPARATUS AND MATERIALS IN THE VISCOSE INDUSTRY
F. Ohl
Chem. Met. Zeits. (Metallborse) V. 22 (1932) 193-194

SPINNERETS
C. L. Moore
Silk and Rayon V. 8 (1934) 72-74

HEAT AND CORROSION RESISTANCE USES

DEVELOPMENT OF THE PLATINUM ALLOY-LINED DIE (for regulating the flow of molten glass)
H. K. Richardson
Jnl. Amer. Ceramic Soc. V. 17 (1934) 236-239

THE MANUFACTURE, FABRICATION AND USES OF GLASS FIBERS
C. Pazsiczky
Glass Tech. Berichte V. 14 (1936) 206-211
Translation by S. R. Scholes—The Glass Industry V. 18 (1937) 17

PROPERTIES OF RARE METALS FOR HIGH TEMPERATURE SERVICE
W. H. Swanger
Am. Soc. Test Mat. and Amer. Soc. Mech. Eng. Symposium on Effect of Temp. on Metals (1931)

NEW TOOLS FOR HIGH TEMPERATURE RESEARCH
R. B. Sosman
Ind. Eng. Chem. V. 23 (1931) 1369-1374

RHODIUM WIRE FOR LABORATORY FURNACES
I. Westermann
Metallwirtschaft V. 11 (1932) 152-153

COMPARISON OF FUSED SILICA, GOLD AND PLATINUM LININGS FOR CALORIMETER BOMBS
O. K. Bates
Ind. Eng. Chem. Analyt. Edition V. 2 (1930) 162-164

THERMOMETRY

TEMPERATURE—ITS MEASUREMENT AND CONTROL IN SCIENCE AND INDUSTRY
Reinhold Pub. Corp. N. Y. (1941)

REFERENCE TABLES FOR PLATINUM TO PLATINUM RHODIUM THERMOCOUPLES
W. F. Roeser and H. T. Wensel
Jnl. Res. Bur. Stds. V. 10 (1933) 275-287

METHODS OF TESTING THERMOCOUPLES AND THERMOCOUPLE MATERIALS
W. F. Roeser and H. T. Wensel
Jnl. Res. Bur. Stds. V. 14 (1933) 247-282

ESTABLISHMENT OF A TEMPERATURE SCALE FOR THE CALIBRATION OF THERMOMETERS BETWEEN 14° AND 83° K.
H. J. Hoge and F. G. Brickwedde—Research Paper R. P. 1188
Jnl. Res. Bur. Stds. V. 22 (1939) 351-373

THE INTERNATIONAL TEMPERATURE SCALE
G. K. Burgess
Jnl. Res. Bur. Stds. V. 1 (1928) 635-640

CATALYSTS

CATALYSTS FOR THE OXIDATION OF AMMONIA TO OXIDES OF NITROGEN
S. L. Handforth and J. N. Tilley
Ind. Eng. Chem. V. 26 (1934) 1287-1292

MANUFACTURE OF NITRIC ACID BY THE OXIDATION OF AMMONIA
G. B. Taylor, T. H. Chilton and S. L. Handforth
Ind. Eng. Chem. V. 23 (1931) 860

THE GAUZE CATALYST IN AMMONIA OXIDATION
G. A. Perley and M. W. Varrell
Ind. Eng. Chem. V. 21 (1929) 222

NITRIC ACID FROM AMMONIA
C. L. Parsons
Ind. Eng. Chem. V. 19 (1927) 789

TEMPERATURE CONTROL IN AMMONIA OXIDATION
G. A. Perley and R. P. Smith
Ind. Eng. Chem. V. 17 (1925) 258

PLATINUM VS VANADIUM PENTOXIDE AS CATALYSTS FOR SULPHURIC ACID MANUFACTURE
A. P. Thompson
Amer. Inst. Chem. Engs. V. 27 1931 pp. 264-290

SULPHURIC ACID MANUFACTURE
A. M. Fairlie
Reinhold Pbl. Co. N. Y. 1936

THE MANUFACTURE OF SULPHURIC ACID: Contact Process Vol. IV of the Lunge Series on the "Manufacture of Acids and Alkalies"
F. D. Miles
Van Nostrand N. Y. 1925

THE MANUFACTURE OF SULPHURIC ACID BY THE CONTACT PROCESS
M. F. Chase and F. E. Pierce
Ind. Eng. Chem. V. 14 (1922) 498

INFLUENCE OF REACTION RATE ON OPERATING CONDITIONS IN CONTACT SULPHURIC ACID MANUFACTURE
W. K. Lewis and E. D. Ries
Ind. Eng. Chem. V. 17 (1925) 593; V. 19 (1927) 830

HYDROGENATION OF ORGANIC SUBSTANCES
C. Ellis
Van Nostrand, N. Y. 1930

BIBLIOGRAPHY OF PATENTS ON PALLADIUM CATALYSTS
Baker and Co., Newark, N. J. 1939

IGNITION OF GAS BY COLD CATALYSTS
L. W. Andrew, A. B. Densham and E. W. Voice
Inst. Gas Engs. London 1937

PLATINIZED SILICA GEL AS OXIDATION CATALYST IN GAS ANALYSIS
K. A. Kobe and E. J. Argeson
Ind. Eng. Chem. (Anal. Ed.) V. 5 (1933) 110-112; V. 6 (1934) 35-37

CONTACTS

ELECTRICAL CONTACTS
G. Windred
Macmillan and Co., London 1940

WEAR OF ELECTRICAL CONTACT POINTS
W. Betteridge and J. A. Laird
Jnl. Inst. Electrical Eng. V. 82 (1938) 625-632

CONTACT METALS AND CONTACT CARE
P. Mabb
Metal Industry (London) V. 43 (1933) 3-5

USE OF NOBLE METALS FOR ELECTRICAL CONTACTS
E. F. Kingsbury
Trans. Amer. Inst. Min. Met. Engrs. V. (1928) 804-824

CONTACTS SUITABLE FOR INSTRUMENTS
H. Williams
Jnl. Scientific Instruments V. 11 (1934) 273

SPARKING AND ARCING AT RELAY CONTACTS AND THE USE OF SPARK QUENCH CIRCUITS
A. H. Jacquest and L. H. Harris
Inst. Post Office Elect. Engs. 1927, Paper No. 118

ELEKTRISCHE KONTAKE
W. Burstyn
Springer, Berlin 1937

PRECIOUS METALS FOR CONTACTS
F. Braby
Electrical Times V. 93 (1938) 2413

SPARK PLUGS

SOME FACTORS CONTROLLING THE DEVELOPMENT OF ELECTRICAL IGNITION OF AERO ENGINES
G. E. Bairstro
Roy. Aeronautical Soc. (London) 1939

AVIATION FUELS AND ENGINES
F. R. Banks
Soc. Auto Engs. Jnl. V. 45 #3 (1939) 389-406

METALLURGY AND THE AERO ENGINE
D. R. Pye
Jnl. Inst. Metals (London) V. 56 (1937) 19-34

ON THE EROSION OF SPARKING PLUG ELECTRODE MATERIALS AND THE VARIATION OF SPARKING PLUG VOLTAGE (A Study of the Factors Affecting the Erosion; does not include Platinum Metal Materials)
W. R. Denenham and F. C. Hayden
Aeronaut Res. Committee Report and Memoranda #1744 London (1936)

DENTAL

PHYSICAL PROPERTIES OF DENTAL MATERIALS
R. L. Coleman
Research Paper 32 Jnl. Res. Bur. Stds. 1928

WROUGHT GOLD WIRE ALLOYS: Physical Properties and a Specification
G. C. Paffenbarger, W. T. Sweeney and A. Isaacs
Jnl. Amer. Dental Asso. V. 19 (1932) 2061-2086

THE ROLE OF PLATINUM METALS IN DENTAL ALLOYS
E. M. Wise, W. S. Crowell and J. T. Eash
Trans. Inst. Min. Met. Engrs. V. 99 (1932) 363-407; V. 104 (1933) 276-303

PLATINUM PALLADIUM GOLD IN DENTISTRY
International Nickel Co., New York, 1937

THE SCIENCE OF DENTAL MATERIALS
E. W. Skinner
W. B. Saunders Co., Philadelphia, Pa. 1936

ALBA DAS ERGEBNIS EINER FORSCHUNG
W. C. Heraeus
Hanau, Germany, 1938

FURTHER REPORT ON PHYSICAL PROPERTIES AND CLINICAL VALUES OF PLATINUM-CENTERED GOLD FOIL AS COMPARED TO PURE GOLD FILLING MATERIALS
R. W. Rule
Jnl. Amer. Dental Asso. V. 24 (1937) 583-595

A METHOD OF IMPROVING THE PROPERTIES OF DENTAL CASTING ALLOYS
A. R. Raper and E. C. Rhodes
Brit. Dental Jnl. V. 61 (1936) 204-211

SHOULDERLESS PORCELAIN JACKET CROWNS WITH REINFORCED PLATINUM MATRIX
D. S. Gardner
J. Amer. Dental Assoc. V. 26 (1939) 744-753

PLATINUM IRIDIUM CASTING: A New Concept of the Dental Casting Process
E. R. Granger
Amer. Acad. Restorative Dentistry July 1939

MISCELLANEOUS

METHODS FOR THE DETECTION AND DETERMINATION OF CARBON MONOXIDE
L. B. Berger and H. H. Schenk
U. S. Bur. Mines Tech. Paper 582 (1938)

USE OF OSMIUM SALTS IN BLOOD ANALYSIS
G. C. von Walsem
Zeits wiss Mikroskop e V. 46 (1936) 478-480

PALLADIUM AND PALLADIUM LEAF
A. B. Thomas
Metal Industry (New York) V. 33 (1935) 354

GLASS TO METAL JOINTS (A method of producing vacuum-tight seals between metal and porcelain)
E. C. McKelvy and C. S. Taylor
Jnl. Amer. Chem. Soc. V. 42 (1920) 1364

1M 3-60 9647

PRINTED IN U.S.A.